Gli Asolani

MCM LIV

PIETRO BEMBO'S

Gli Asolani

Translated by

RUDOLF B. GOTTFRIED

Indiana University Press

BLOOMINGTON · 1954

INDIANA UNIVERSITY PUBLICATIONS
HUMANITIES SERIES NO. 31
Indiana University, Bloomington, Indiana

Edward D. Seeber, Editor
David H. Dickason, Assistant Editor
Agapito Rey, Assistant Editor

The Indiana University Publications, Humanities Series,
was founded in 1939 for the publication of occasional papers
and monographs by faculty members.

Contents

INTRODUCTION

IF ANY readers of *Gli Asolani* visit Asolo itself, they will
find that the topography of the region dramatically reveals one difference between the age of Pietro Bembo
and their own. Bembo carefully describes the garden in
which his dialogues take place: the steps descending from
the palace of the Queen, the formal pattern of arbor,
hedge, and wall, the two marble windows opening on the
wide Trevisan plain below, the fountain around which his
gentlemen and ladies gather in the laurels' shade; and as a
pendent scene he later shows the little wooded mountaintop where Lavinello meets a hermit. Today, though the
garden and much of the palace have not existed for more
than a century, it is still possible to reconstruct that setting
while one is standing on the spot; and the imagination may
even identify Lavinello's mountaintop with the Colle di
San Martino, the highest point on the line of foothills
along which the scattered town is built. But these recog-
nitions are not so telling as another, the discovery that
Bembo's Asolo faces southward, across the plain to
Venice, and that Bembo turns his back on the dominant
feature of the landscape, the great wall of the Alps, and
in particular on the towering front of Monte Grappa
which rises only a few miles to the north. What he omits

from the scene is precisely what a modern eye selects as its most striking element.

In a similar way, modern Asolo is dominated by the Grappa of Victorian enthusiasts, Robert Browning; and one must resolutely turn his back on that familiar outline if he would discuss, however briefly, the human setting, writing, publication, and literary significance of *Gli Asolani*.

Caterina Cornaro, who is the presiding figure on Bembo's stage, became Queen of Cyprus and Lady of Asolo through a series of tragic circumstances. The daughter of an aristocratic Venetian family, in 1472 she was married, for reasons of state, to Giacomo II, King of Cyprus. Within three years both her husband and her infant son had died; nevertheless, in spite of revolution and dynastic conflict, she contrived to govern the island until the beginning of 1489, when the rulers of Venice, again for reasons of state, decided that it would be expedient for her to abdicate her crown if not her title. A few months later, after her return to Italy, she received the lordship of Asolo as a recompense; and there she maintained her court until 1509, a year before her death.[1] Bembo, her younger kinsman, visited her at Asolo in 1495 while she was celebrating the marriage of a favorite maid of honor, one Fiammetta; and this may well have been the occasion which supplied the initial inspiration for *Gli Asolani*.[2]

[1] See Roberto Cessi, "Caterina Cornaro," *Enciclopedia Italiana* (Istituto Giovanni Trecanni, 1929–49).

[2] D. Carlo G. Bernardi, *Guida Storico-Turistico-Sentimentale di Asolo* (Milan, 1949), Part I, p. 40.

Bembo's own career, aside from domestic losses like that of his brother Carlo, seems to have been peculiarly fortunate. Born in 1470, he belonged to a large and powerful Venetian house. Although he was only eight years old when his father became ambassador to Florence, the two years which the boy spent in that city probably contributed to his later zeal for the literary heritage of the great Tuscan writers. As he grew older, he received a thoroughgoing humanistic education, meeting Politian at Venice in 1491, in the next year studying Greek at Messina under Lascaris, and, again at Venice, joining the Filelleni group which gathered around Aldus when he began to publish in 1493. Yet Bembo also participated in the court life of the period, not only at Asolo but at Ferrara, where his father served as Venetian co-ruler in 1497, and at Urbino, where the social and cultural refinements of the age were carried to their apogee during the very years of Bembo's stay (1506–1512). With the accession of Leo X in 1513, the already well-known courtier-humanist became a Papal secretary and formed a liaison with a young woman named Morosina, who eventually bore him three children. Meanwhile, having departed from Rome in 1519, he spent a number of years in scholarly retirement near Padua; there, in his capacity of Historiographer of Venice, he prepared a Latin account of the city's recent history and in 1525 published one of his two most important Italian works, *Le Prose della Volgar Lingua*, a treatise which argues that the Italian writers of his time should use the Tuscan of Petrarch and Boccaccio rather than the various contemporary dialects. In 1538, three years after Morosina's death, his attainments were at last rewarded by election to the College of Cardinals; and before his own death in 1547 he was also preferred to the Bishopric of Gubbio.[3]

Bembo had what is surely one of the richest careers of the Italian Renaissance. To have lived in the Florence of Lorenzo the Magnificent, the Venice of Aldus, and the Rome of Leo X; to have been portrayed in youth by Bellini and in old age by Titian; to have known Raphael, Vittoria Colonna, Politian, Erasmus, and Pietro Aretino; to have been chosen by Castiglione as his mouthpiece when he reached the climax of *The Courtier;* to have written two of the most famous treatises and the best Petrarchan verse of the sixteenth century; to have experienced first physical and romantic passion, then the responsibilities of parenthood through a liaison which resembled marriage, and finally the spiritual honors belonging to a bishop and a cardinal:—it is not an exaggeration to say that Bembo both had his cake and ate it several times.

Gli Asolani belongs to the early period during which Bembo repeatedly succumbed to physical and romantic passion. Between 1495, the date at which he probably, as we have seen, began to frame his work, and 1505, the year of its first publication, he must have fallen in and out of love with at least three women.[4] With the first of these, an unidentified Venetian, known as "M. G.," who was probably of lower social rank and without Bembo's literary interests, he seems to have been involved in 1497 and

---

[3] See Mario Santoro, *Pietro Bembo* (Naples, 1937), *passim.*
[4] Santoro, pp. 15-24.

1498.[5] The second love affair produced a series of seventy-seven letters which Bembo wrote to another Venetian woman in 1500 and 1501 and which his executors published five years after his death; quite recently her side of the correspondence, preserved and annotated by Bembo himself, has been discovered and published; it reveals that this second inamorata, named Maria Savorgnan, was a married woman of the upper middle class who cultivated the Petrarchan aspects of her relation, equivocal as that relation was, with the young man of letters.[6] In the third place, Bembo engaged in his well-known amour with Lucrezia Borgia, already married to Alfonso d'Este and soon to be Duchess of Ferrara; their passion, which ran its course between 1502 and 1505, is shown by their surviving letters to have been warm, though it may not be true, as Will Cuppy notes, that while her husband was away, "Lucrezia would slip on something comfortable and curl up with a good author." [7] Each of these love affairs, it is well to add, has its bearing on *Gli Asolani*.

In a letter dated from Ferrara on December 11, 1497, after writing that he spends the hours before dawn as well as most of his mornings in work on *Gli Asolani*, Bembo speaks of the wound from which he suffers, presumably his separation from the first of his three mistresses; and it seems clear that the tragic view of love which Perottino expounds in the opening dialogue of the book embodies

[5] Pietro Bembo, *Opere* (Venice, 1729), III, 102.

[6] See *Opere*, III, 343–75; Maria Savorgnan and Pietro Bembo, *Carteggio d'Amore*, ed. Carlo Dionisotti (Florence, 1950).

[7] *The Decline and Fall of Practically Everybody* (New York, 1950), p. 104. See *Opere*, III, 309–17, 375–80, 501–4; IV, 174–5, 345–6.

Bembo's dissatisfaction with this first affair.[8] At any rate, his correspondence with Maria Savorgnan shows that he later assumed the name of Perottino in wooing his second mistress and that she followed the composition of *Gli Asolani* with keen interest; in a letter dated May 30, 1500, but probably written some months later, he refers to Book Two, and on January 4, 1501, he sends her Lavinello's *canzoni* from Book Three, although only the first of them is yet amended; on two occasions the desire to read "el vostro libro" together seems to have served as Maria's excuse to her husband for being closeted with her lover; and there is an intimate stylistic similarity between their correspondence and *Gli Asolani*.[9] That work must, in any case, have been substantially completed by December 24, 1502, when Bembo asks to have a friend return the manuscript with suggested changes.[10]

Meanwhile, however, he had met Lucrezia; and by July, 1503, she appears to have known at least part of *Gli Asolani*.[11] When he left Ferrara at the end of 1503, he promised to send her the whole; but the death of his

[8] *Opere*, IV, 165; Dionisotti in *Carteggio*, p. xxiv. Another letter shows that the work was half completed by December 3, 1498; for this and other data on composition see *Gli Asolani e le Rime*, ed. Carlo Dionisotti-Casalone (Turin, 1932), pp. 297–300.

[9] *Carteggio*, pp. 133, 65, 124, 6, 26, xxiv. That *Gli Asolani* was woven on the warp of reality is further indicated by Bembo's references to a boy called "Lavinello" (*Opere*, III, 98–9) and his attempt to secure a medal representing the real woman who is introduced as Berenice in the book, apparently a certain Berenice Gambara (*Carteggio*, p. xx; *Opere*, III, 221, 502).

[10] *Opere*, III, 99.

[11] Maria Bellonci, *Lucrezia Borgia, La Sua Vita e i Suoi Tempi* (Verona, 1947), pp. 391–4, 427; *Opere*, III, 502.

brother Carlo on December 30 threw all his affairs into confusion, and it was not until August 1, 1504, that the work was dispatched to her with the dedication which was printed in the earliest editions. This is a revealing document. It compares his loss of Carlo to the two blows which Lucrezia has lately suffered, one of them undoubtedly the death of her illustrious father, Pope Alexander VI, on August 18, 1503, and the other perhaps that of her child on September 5, 1502.[12] Bembo goes on to mention the recent marriage of her maid of honor Nicola which is parallel to that of Caterina Cornaro's maid of honor in *Gli Asolani*, just as Angela Borgia (whose flirtations later caused a bloody quarrel among the brothers of the Duke) corresponds to Caterina's ladies and the courtiers Tebaldeo and Strozzi to Perottino, Gismondo, and Lavinello; thus Asolo becomes Ferrara.[13] But it is an even greater shock to read, in the final sentences of the dedication, that Lucrezia is a miracle of inner virtue as well as of external beauty, though the novelty of the idea is softened if we may assume that Bembo is alluding to their hidden love when he speaks of the pleasure she enjoys within her mind.[14]

In the following months, it is evident, Lucrezia urged that *Gli Asolani* should be published; [15] yet it was March, 1505, according to the colophon, before Aldus issued the book in Venice. Its steady, if not immediate popularity is revealed by the fact that it was reprinted at least seven

[12] Bellonci, p. 378.
[13] Bembo was on very friendly terms with Nicola (*Opere*, III, 501).
[14] Bellonci, p. 427.
[15] *Opere*, III, 312–3.

times during the next seventeen years. Then, at some date not earlier than 1525, Bembo undertook a complete revision of the text; and in 1530 this was published by Sabbio in Venice as the so-called "second" edition. The revision included an infinite number of small verbal changes and one important addition, a discourse on the Thomist distinction between love and desire; but its most striking feature is the omission of certain considerable passages, namely, the dedication to Lucrezia, four poems containing a total of 111 lines, and, in prose, a five-page account of a conversation in which Gismondo asked his lady how she would act if he were dead, a description of the ring she gave him, a refutation of the charge that love causes bitter memories, and a long reference to the story of Cimon in Boccaccio (*Decameron*, V, 1). These changes, which are improvements for the most part, were followed in three reprints issued during Bembo's lifetime; but before he died, he made more than 150 further revisions in this text, revisions which were included in Scotto's Venice edition of 1553 and in at least nine other reprints before the end of the sixteenth century.[16]

By 1600 there were thus at least twenty-two Italian editions of *Gli Asolani*. A Spanish version appeared at Salamanca in 1551; and the French translation of Jean Martin which was first published in 1545 was later reprinted at least six times.[17] Therefore, even though it does

[16] For the material in this paragraph see *Opere*, II, 68 (of *Asolani* section); Dionisotti-Casalone in *Gli Asolani e le Rime*, pp. 297–300; and the catalogues of the British Museum, Bibliothèque Nationale, and Library of Congress.

[17] A French translation was already being made in 1508 (*Opere*, III, 117).

not seem to have been translated into English, we are justified in calling *Gli Asolani* one of the influential books of
the Renaissance and in considering the direction of that
influence.

Those who know Bembo's name but not his work are
apt to think of him as he is described by his friend
Castiglione in *The Courtier*, a book of deeper insight and
more human interest than anything which Bembo ever
wrote. Castiglione, writing some years after the event,
recounts, or pretends to recount, what was said during
four evenings at the court of Urbino in March, 1507;
Bembo, who is present throughout the dialogues, takes
a leading rôle only at the very end of the last evening
when the Duchess assigns him the task of telling the others
what kind of love is suitable for the Courtier. In what
follows he reveals that he is a master of the art of raillery
and too much a man of the world to take himself over-
seriously; nevertheless Castiglione has Bembo deliver a
highly serious, at times almost mystical exposition of the
Platonic doctrine of love as understood by the Renaissance: the divine origin of beauty, the distinction between
the worlds of sense and intellect, the various steps by
which the sensual love of one lady is finally transformed
into the spiritual love of God. And a reference to
Lavinello's hermit clearly relates this passage to the second half of Book Three, the corresponding climax of *Gli
Asolani.*

Is Castiglione right in placing this emphasis on Bembo's
Platonism? That he was right might be argued from the
fact that Bembo read and apparently criticized the manu-

script of *The Courtier* before it was published by Aldus in 1528.[18] But in 1528, when he was fifty-eight years old, he may very well have been contented to appear more Platonic than he had really been when he was thirty-seven; and there is evidence to support this deduction. For the Carnival at Urbino in 1507, celebrated at almost the very moment which *The Courtier* describes, Bembo composed certain "Stanze" which he and Ottaviano Fregoso, disguised as ambassadors from Venus, recited to the Duchess and Emilia Pia before the assembled court.[19] The poem is a graceful plea for natural love, the kind of love which, as we are told, made Catullus write of Lesbia and Ovid of Corinna; it contains nothing which is distinctively Platonic; in fact, it expresses the point of view of the hedonist Gismondo rather than of Lavinello.

If we turn to the still younger Bembo who produced *Gli Asolani*, his Platonism appears to be an even more doubtful quantity than in 1507. The three love affairs which nourished his treatise could hardly, at best, evoke a sincere devotion to heavenly beauty; and it is not surprising to find him writing to the Duchess of Urbino on March 20, 1504, that the thought of heavenly things had never occupied him much and did not occupy him now at all.[20] When *Gli Asolani* was published a year later, it revealed, in spite of appearances to the contrary, that this was true. Both Perottino's eloquent attack and Gismondo's warm eulogy on earthly love carry a tone of conviction which it is hard to catch in Lavinello's Platonic resolution

[18] See *Opere*, III, 119.
[19] *Opere*, II, 37–40 (of *Rime* section); III, 201–2.
[20] *Opere*, III, 320.

of the problem in Book Three. That book is shorter than the other two; and the first half of it, in which Lavinello denies the validity of his friends' positions and recites three *canzoni* in honor of his lady, is only distantly Platonic (the lady, for example, remains an individual throughout the poems). The second half, the report on his conversation with the hermit, brings us to the kind of Platonism which Bembo was given to explain in *The Courtier*, and Castiglione clearly owes a debt to the ideas expressed in these concluding pages of *Gli Asolani*; but a comparison also reveals that in some things (as, for example, in explaining how love ascends from individual to universal beauty) *The Courtier* is much closer to Plato than *Gli Asolani* is. It becomes evident that the Platonic tradition, however distorted and diluted by the Renaissance, had a more genuine representative in Castiglione than in Bembo.

This conclusion is borne out by Bembo's revisions in *Gli Asolani* of 1530. The considerable omissions previously noted all occur in Books One and Two, the non-Platonic portion of the work; but they seem to have been made chiefly in order to render the three books more nearly equal in length: that is, for a literary rather than a philosophical reason. Thus, the only considerable addition is made in Book Three, the shortest of the books; and the added passage, in which the hermit draws the Thomist distinction between love and desire, is actually a correction of what Lavinello has already said and an intrusion in the Platonic context.

Platonism is, on the whole, a literary rather than a philosophical element in *Gli Asolani*; it contributes more to the form than to the substance of the treatise. The real content of most of Bembo's pages is derived from experience, from the courtly framework of the *Decameron*, and from the modified Petrarchan tradition which also appears in his correspondence with Maria Savorgnan, a tradition which subordinated philosophical ideas to the various and often contradictory moods of earthly love. From his study of the *Dialogues*, on the other hand, Bembo gained not merely the arguments of Lavinello's hermit or an occasional reference like Gismondo's to the myth that every pair of lovers was at first a single creature, but a perception of what might be done with the dialogue as a literary form. He is indebted to Plato, not so much for the arguments of Lavinello's hermit as for the use of that curious figure, on the model of Diotima, to secure an almost supernatural climax; and Plato's influence is even more significantly revealed in Bembo's constant effort to develop ideas through conversation and to give his discussions as much dramatic variety as possible. *Gli Asolani* is, therefore, the artistic rather than the intellectual fruit of those Platonic studies which the Florentine Academy had made a generation earlier. Not that Bembo plays an unimportant rôle: without his dialogues we might never have had the finer art of Castiglione.

A NOTE ON THIS TRANSLATION

GLI ASOLANI, as far as I can determine, has never been entirely translated into English before, although one lyric, "Voi mi ponese in foco" (see pp. 35–36), was paraphrased by Wyatt [21] and another, "Quand'io penso al martire,"

[21] *Collected Poems*, ed. Kenneth Muir (London, 1949), pp. 93–4.

was borrowed in the second part of *Don Quixote* (p. 33, chap. 68) from the Spanish version of 1551 and consequently appears in all the English versions of Cervantes' masterpiece. This neglect of Bembo's treatise as a whole deprives me of the traditional opportunity to uncover the crimes of some immediate benefactor. Nevertheless, the modern translations of various other works have provoked me into a philosophy of my own: I feel that a literal version of an elaborate prose can be only spineless and insipid and that in translating poetry into poetry one generally runs the opposite hazard of deviating too widely from the thought and imagery of the original. Accordingly, I have taken almost Elizabethan liberties with Bembo's prose, omitting repetitious phrases, at times simplifying his sentence structure, and breaking his lengthy paragraphs down into more readable units, yet never, I hope, misrepresenting his sense or losing the somewhat self-conscious elegance which must have impressed contemporary readers of his Tuscan style. In dealing with the poetry, on the other hand, I have endeavored to reproduce Bembo's meaning, phraseology, and verse forms as closely as possible, although the precise meaning and phraseology must frequently, of course, be sacrificed if one is to preserve the verse forms. In only two cases, I should add, has it been necessary to depart from the original rhyme schemes: The fourth and eighth lines of each stanza in one brief canzone (p. 83) contain internal rhymes which I have had to omit. In another canzone (pp. 102–4) the rhymes occur, not between lines within each stanza, but between the corresponding lines of all the stanzas (the actual rhyme scheme, modeled on

Petrarch's *Rime*, no. 29, is *abcdefg abcdefg abcdefg abcdefg abcdefg abcdefg abcdefg abcdefg fg*); given the poverty of English in rhyme sounds, I have been content to use them to link merely each pair of stanzas in this poem.

The definitive text of *Gli Asolani*, that of 1553, is the basis of my translation; but from the original text of 1505 I have likewise included Bembo's dedication to Lucrezia Borgia.

I am grateful to the Graduate School of Indiana University, which defrayed the cost of having my manuscript typed. To the editors of *The Folio: A Magazine for Writers* I am indebted for their kind permission to republish the verse translation "Lady, you've set me all afire." And for the device of an anchor dolphin-twined, which appears on the half title, I am obviously indebted to Aldus, who was indebted for that trademark to a Roman coin which Bembo gave him; but none of us has ever reproduced it by permission.

R. B. G.

TO THE LADY LUCREZIA
D'ESTE BORGIA
THE MOST ILLUSTRIOUS DUCHESS
OF FERRARA
FROM PIETRO BEMBO

IF I HAVE not already sent Your Highness those discourses which I promised, last year in Ferrara, that I would send you as soon as I reached here, the loss of my dear brother Carlo, whom, contrary to all expectation, I found to have passed from life, may serve as my apology. His death so stupefied me that, like those who remain without feeling long after they have been stricken by arrows, I have not yet been able to turn my mind to anything but my deep, incurable wound. For I have lost not merely a brother,—a bereavement which is wont in any case to be heavy and grievous of itself,—but an only brother who had just entered the first flowering of his youth and who, out of his great love for me making every wish of mine his own, had no greater care than to relieve me of all my cares, so that I might give my whole time and thought to the literary studies which he knew were dear to me above everything; a brother, moreover, of a bright and noble spirit, worthy for his many parts to reach the years of bended age, to whom it was at least fitting that, as he had entered life later than I, he should quit it after me. But how much all these things have continually deepened my wound, Your Highness may easily estimate from those two blows which a malicious fortune has dealt to you in so short a space of time.

Now, since I can do no otherwise and, through the common, ordinary medicine afforded by this interval rather than by any other remedy, my grief and tears have partly given way to reason and clear thinking, I remember my debt and the promise made to Your Highness, and send these discourses, such as they are, to you, and all the more readily at this time as I have recently learned that Your Highness has married off your worthy Nicola. For I consider them no unseemly gift at such a season, when, although my employments now prevent me from taking part in your celebrations, these may speak and argue in my place with Your Highness, with your dear and worthy Lady Angela Borgia, and with the bride, perhaps not without the assistance of Master Ercole Strozzi and Master Antonio Tebaldeo, the familiars and followers of Your Highness, much loved of me and honored by the world. And it may well be that the very things which other young men have discussed with other ladies during the festivities for another marriage, you in your festivities will read with your maids of honor and courtiers, as they have been written down by me, who am likewise yours.

This you will perchance do joyfully, as one who, longing rather to dress out her soul with comely virtues than to cover her body with precious clothes, devotes whatever time she can to reading or writing something; so, much as your beauty surpasses that of other ladies, the attractions of your mind may eclipse those of your body, and you may become, as it were, greater than yourself, loving far rather to receive an inward pleasure than to please all others outwardly (though it be infinitely pleasing to them). And I shall consider myself to have received a very satisfactory reward for this youthful toil of mine if I may believe that, when you read these words, by virtue of the things discussed in them you may become still more devoted to that so high and praiseworthy wish of yours. To whose good graces I commend myself most humbly.

Venice, August 1, 1504

GLI ASOLANI
BY MASTER PIETRO BEMBO
IN WHICH LOVE IS
THE SUBJECT OF DISCOURSE

Book One

AT NIGHT, when weary mariners are hard-driven by a
dark and cloudy tempest and they can glimpse no star
nor anything which might serve to guide their course,
they are accustomed to recover north by studying the In-
dian lodestone; thus, knowing what wind buffets them,
they do not lose the power to make both sail and rudder
speed them to their port, or at least to some point of
greater safety. And when those who travel through an
unknown country alight, doubtful and uncertain, beside
a fork where many similar roads take their beginning and
they cannot discern the right one, they are glad to meet
some man who tells them which way will lead them, perhaps before night falls, directly to their inn.

For this reason, judging by the daily course of things
how few are those who do not practice an almost constant
trade of calamity and care, since the pilgrimage of this
mortal life of ours is now blown upon by passions, now
made doubtful by opinions which bear a delusive similarity to truth, I have always felt that they perform a
gracious office who, by discussing things they have experienced or learned from others or found out by them-

selves, show other men how not to wander in so dangerous a course or lose a path so easily forsaken. For what act can be more gracious than to help another? or what can be done on earth which is more suitable to man than to procure the good of many men? And so, if it is praise-worthy in itself for one man alone, unseen and unrecog-nized by anyone, to be able to live blameless (which is indeed most praiseworthy), how much more ought he to be admired who can not only guide his own life without fault but also teach an infinite number of other men the means to shun their failings?

But among the first of many causes which disturb our tranquil voyage and make us suspicious and uncertain of the path of virtuous living is wont to be our ignorance, for the most part, as to what love is good, what evil; an ig-norance which harasses and bewilders our lives since we love the things from which we ought to flee, do not love those we ought to seek, and sometimes shun or pursue them less or more than is becoming. On the subject of love I have therefore undertaken to gather certain dis-courses which three of our wise and well-informed young men, speaking a few days ago before a company of three excellent young ladies and, for a time, in the presence of my lady the Queen of Cyprus, diversely argued on three separate occasions. Thus the no little profit and enjoyment I received from hearing them may be extended, now that they are published, to any other whom it would have pleased to hear them.

In doing which, although it is well at every age to hear and read useful things, and particularly a discussion of this subject, for at no season is it possible not to know love of some kind since nature has given all men, along with life, the faculty of ever loving one thing or another, yet I, who am still a youth, comfort and exhort young men and young women chiefly. Thus, many of them, when they have learned what I engage to write, will perhaps easily be able to form an opinion of love before they have themselves made proof of it.

At present I shall not venture to say how valuable this must be to them; they can determine it more justly in their later and much riper years. But as experience is indeed the best and most dependable teacher in most things, so in some, especially in those which can cause no less disquietude than pleasure (and this matter of love is evidently such), there is no doubt that many have often found it very useful to learn by reading or consulting others before coming to the touch themselves. It may therefore be called a splendid rediscovery of men which written works provide. In them, seeing as in a mirror many outworn things which could not otherwise have reached our knowledge, we may select the one which fits our case and, having been instructed by the example of others, may more securely, like experienced pilots and travelers, set forth upon seas which we have never furrowed and paths as yet untrodden. Nor should I fail to mention the infinite pleasure procured by various studies, on which the minds of some men are often fed as the body is on food, imbibing with them a most delightful nourishment.

But to lay this matter aside and take in hand the discourses of love already mentioned: in order that it may be better understood exactly how each part was reasoned, I believe it would be well for me, before going on to them, to describe how the whole discussion happened to take place.

The fair and pleasant castle of Asolo, built in the foothills of our mountains overlooking the marches of Treviso, belongs, as everyone should know, to my lady the Queen of Cyprus (with her family, which goes by the name of Cornelia and is much honored in our city of Venice, my own is joined by blood as well as friendship and familiarity). At Asolo, where she went for her diversion last September, it befell that she married off one of her maids of honor, a beautiful, well-bred, gentle girl whom the Queen, having brought her up from childhood, cherished with a most tender love. Accordingly she had preparations made there for a large and brilliant wedding; and after all the more eminent men of the surrounding country had been invited with their ladies, and those of Venice likewise, to the full satisfaction of them all she prolonged the celebrations day after day with music, singing, dancing, and most solemn feasts.

Here, among the others whom the Queen had bidden to these festivities, were three gentlemen of our city, high-spirited and young, who, having been inured to literary studies since their earliest years, still gave most of their time to them and furthermore revealed that pre-eminence in all fair practices which belongs to youths of noble birth. The distinction of their families and even more the living fame which they had won by their studies and their valor endeared them to all the ladies present at the gatherings; yet it chanced that to three fair and amiable young women these gentlemen devoted themselves more often and more confidently than to the others since they were related to them by blood and enjoyed a long familiarity with them and with their husbands, the three of whom had already returned to Venice on affairs. In sweet and honest discourse with these ladies they would be ever drawing out the pleasant time, although Perottino (for so I am minded to call one of them in this work) spoke little and that rarely, nor was he seen, if only once, to have a smile upon his lips throughout those revels. Indeed he often stole far away from everybody, like one whose thoughts were always steeped in sorrow; nor would he have joined the discussions if he had not been urged to do so by his companions, who zealously endeavored to cheer him up by keeping him in happy company.

Nor have I given a fictitious name of this kind to Perottino alone, but to each of the three ladies and the other young men as well, lest, if their real names were known, the light-headed multitude might fancy things somewhat unsuited to the honesty of their lives; for these rumors, passing from one to another, may soon become the common talk of men, not a few of whom are wont, in general, to scan things wholesome with an eye which is unwholesome.

But to return to the wedding celebrations provided by the Queen: They went forward as I have said, until one day after dinner, which was always splendid, being enlivened with various interludes of the kind to win our laughter, with the music of diverse instruments, and with songs now of one manner, now another,—two charming girls, holding each other by the hand, in joyful manner came to the head of the table, where the Queen was seated, and reverently kneeled to her in salutation. Then

both arising, the elder laid to her breast a graceful lute
which she held in one hand and, having touched the
strings with mastery and for a while made pleasing music,
sang in a voice which sweetly harmonized with it:

When I was young, my happy thoughts would soar,
  Rejoicing that my fortune should be such;
  Now Love afflicts and tortures me so much
  That torture can avail him little more.
Luckless, I thought that from the first my suing
  In Love's court would yield a life of pleasure;
  Now dreary death, I know, will be my measure.
  How my credulity was my undoing!
Medea, not yet committed to Love's power,
  Colchis beheld as one carefree and glad;
  But once she burned for Jason, harsh and sad
  Was all her life until its final hour.

    When her friend had completed this song and played
a short transition leading back to the first notes again, the
younger girl, giving them another meaning, made her
sweet response:

When I was young, I used to grieve and long,
  With both my fortune and myself distraught;
  Now Love breathes in my mind so sweet a thought
  I spend my days in laughter and in song.
I would have sworn, Love, that to join your train
  Meant nothing but to founder on the reef;
  Yet even where I feared most harm and grief,
  I find the very remedy for pain.
Till the first day Love drew his bow upon her,

Andromeda felt only sorrow and annoy;
When Perseus won her heart, delight and joy
Were hers while living, and dead, eternal honor.

The two girls, having sung their songs, to which everyone had listened with the most attentive silence, wished
to depart in order to leave room for other entertainment.
Then a maid of honor, one of exceptional beauty and indeed, in the opinion of all beholders, more beautiful than
any other at the celebrations, the same who always served
the Queen with drink when she dined by herself, was
summoned by her mistress and commanded to match those
songs with one of hers. Thus, taking a viola of marvelous
tone, yet not without a blush to find she must perform
so in the public eye, to which she was unused, she sang
this little song to such a fresh and pleasing melody that,
beside the sweet flame her notes enkindled in the listeners'
hearts, those of the other girls left only cold and lifeless
cinders there:

O Love, thy bountihood
  Is not by world or common folk believed,
  Who, being self-deceived,
  Pursue their harm and flee the proffered good.
  But if thy works were no worse understood
  Among us here than where thy splendor throws
  Its unabated ray,
  Our life would take the way
  Of upright wisdom which it now foregoes,
  And with primeval beauty be renewed
  The Golden Age, the old beatitude.

Now the Queen was ever wont, when dinner and the entertainment of eye and ear were over, to withdraw with her maidens to her apartments and there to sleep or do what pleased them most, passing the warmest part of the day in privacy, while the other ladies were free to suit their fancies till, when the evening came, it was time to celebrate once more; then all the ladies and gentlemen would gather with their followers in the great halls of the palace, where they gaily danced and all those things were done which are usual at the revels of a queen. Therefore, when the maiden and the two girls had sung these songs and all the rest of the amusements had been brought to an end, Her Majesty, arising from the others, as usual betook herself to her apartments, and everyone likewise withdrew; but the three ladies of whom I have spoken remained by chance until the end, conversing with their young gentlemen as they roved up and down the banquet chamber. Carried thus by both their phrases and their feet, in a remote corner they came upon a portico which overlooked a lovely garden of the palace.

When they had stood here to marvel at the attractions of this view and, by allowing their eyes to run over now one part, now another, had somewhat satisfied their first desire to gaze upon it, Gismondo, who was the gayest of the company and always ready to amuse the ladies in some honorable way, turned to them, saying, "To sleep after dinner at this hour of the day, my dear young women, may be good at any season of the year; in summer, at any rate, when the days are longest, it can do no harm, if our eyes are willing, to take a pleasant little nap. But by this month it begins to lose much of its previous attractiveness and to become more injurious day by day. So, if you want to take my advice for once, instead of shutting yourselves up in your rooms to nap at this hour, I would suggest that we let sleep lie behind the curtains of our beds and go ourselves into the garden. There we may sit on the fresh grass in the shade and pass this weary subdivision of the day in story-telling or in talking of agreeable things, until the hour for renewing our celebrations summons us indoors with the others to do honor to our bride."

Gismondo's counsels pleased the ladies, who liked the shady trees and the solid discourse of these young men much more than slumber in the royal sheets and the babble of the other women; so all three of them, descending the long steps in festive gaiety, entered the garden with him and his companions.

This garden was of surpassing charm and beauty: In addition to a fair pergola of vines whose broad and shady structure divided it in the middle like a cross, a long and spacious walk, which was bestrewed with shining flint and might be entered at various places, ran around the perimeter. Except where there was an opening into the pergola, this alley was fenced on its inner side by a hedge of very thick, green junipers whose tops might have reached the breast of one who had approached them in order to enjoy the scene, which was equally agreeable in every part. Along the outer edge time-honored laurels, standing much taller than the junipers and half-overarching the pathway with their upper boughs, grew so close and neatly pruned that not one leaf appeared to desire any place but that assigned to it; nor did they reveal any part of the wall behind them except, at either end of one side, the milk-white marble of two ample windows. From these, if one sat within them, as the great thickness of the structure here allowed, he could send his eye far out across the plain, which they commanded from aloft.

When the eager ladies had entered one side of the garden by this fair path and with their young men strolled along it out of all danger from the sun, studying and admiring now this, now that, and chattering of many things, at the farther end they reached a little glade of tender grass, all carpeted with many sorts of charming flowers. Beyond this the laurels, which here grew lawlessly in greater quantity than elsewhere, formed two groves of equal size, black with shade and reverent in their solitude; and deep between them harbored a delightful fountain, carved with consummate art out of the living rock with which the mountain closed the garden on this side. A little stream of clear, fresh water, gushing from the slope, fell into the fountain and from that, which stood at no great height above the earth, descended with a gentle sound into a miniature canal of marble which divided the glade; there received, murmuring and almost hidden in the grass, it hurried on into the garden.

This retreat pleased the fair ladies exceedingly. When each of them had praised it, Madame Berenice, who was a little older than the other two and therefore respected as their leader, looking at Gismondo, said, "Alas, how wrong of us not to have come here all these days! The hours when the bride and the Queen were in retirement we would have passed far better in this spot than in our rooms. Now, Gismondo, since we are here rather through your discernment than our own, decide where you would like us to sit down; for the sun, which, as you see, maliciously pries everywhere, forbids us to inspect the other parts of the garden."

"Madame," replied Gismondo, "it would seem to me that we ought not to spurn this fountain by which you would be so pleased to stay. Here the grass grows more willingly than elsewhere and is more richly dyed with flowers. These trees will also guard us from the sun so well that, for all his power, he never will approach us here this afternoon."

"Then let's sit down," said Madame Berenice; "wherever you please, there let it be. And that no part of your advice may be neglected: here where the murmur of the water stimulates discourse and these dark shadows listen to our words, prepare to tell us of what you would prefer our talk to be. For we are always glad to hear you; and since you have found so sweet a place for our discussions, it is only right that you should choose their subject."

After Madame Berenice had said these words and each of the other two invited Gismondo to speak, he cheerfully replied, "As you have offered me this pre-eminence, I shall accept it." And they having formed a circle in the grass, one seated near the graceful fountain, the others underneath the shady laurels on either bank of the little stream, Gismondo carefully sat down and, glancing pleasantly around on his fair audience, began: "All of us, my lovely ladies, have heard the two girls and the charming maid of honor who in the presence of the Queen, before the tables were removed, sang their three songs so en-

chantingly, two praising and the other mourning love.
Now I am certain that whoever complains of love and
slanders it knows neither the nature of things nor its
peculiar quality, and wanders far from the straight and
narrow road of truth. So should any of you, fair ladies,
or of us (and I know there are such), agree with the first
singer that love is not a goodly thing, let him, in order
that I may answer, declare what he believes and hearten
me to show him how greatly this opinion has beguiled
him to his own undoing. If you agree to this, as you ought
certainly to do, and if you still wish that I should hold
the leadership which you have already bestowed on me,
we shall have a fair and spacious field for this day's talk."
And having spoken thus, he fell silent.

When Gismondo's proposal had been heard, the honorable ladies hung fire for the moment; and now Madame
Berenice half repented in her mind for having licensed
him to speak too freely. Yet considering that he, albeit
an amorous and pleasant bachelor, was never immodest
in his speech, she reassured herself and began to smile
with her companions, who, likewise reassured after their
brief hesitation, perceived from Gismondo's words that
he assailed the savage grief of Perottino and would provoke him into speaking; for they knew that the latter
never spoke other than evil of love's work. But since
Perottino, for all that, made no reply and uttered not a
syllable, Gismondo began again: "It is no wonder if you
are silent, my sweet young women; for I believe that since
love can never in any wise have served you ill, you would
exert yourselves rather to praise him than to blame, were
it not that a becoming modesty, always commendable

in a lady, had restrained you (though it is always possible to hold the most virtuous discourse on love). But I marvel greatly at my companions, who, even though they believed the very opposite, ought at least to decry that quality by way of jest, in order that we might debate so excellent a theme among us here today. Not that they should do that either, for by good luck there is one seated beside us whom prejudice has really convinced that love is evil and yet who holds his peace."

Then Perottino, who could not continue to hide and whose face revealed a kind of dismay, broke his long silence by saying, "I am well aware, Gismondo, that it is me you summon to this encounter; but I'm too lame a barb for such a course. You would do better to challenge the ladies and Lavinello and me, if you wish, on other ground and to allow us an arena less flinty and unpleasing."

At this point much was said by Gismondo and Lavinello, the third of the young men, urging Perottino to speak; but he stood his ground in obstinate refusal. When Madame Berenice and her companions saw this, all of them began to importune him to say something for their common satisfaction and out of love for them, since they desired to hear him; and now one, now another, they so assailed him with their honeyed words that in the end he was overcome and surrendered in these terms: "To be silent and to speak have at this moment become equally distasteful to me because I neither ought to do the one nor wish to do the other. But now, ladies, the scale is tipped by that reverence I must feel for your commands, if not for those of Gismondo. Should he propose a better subject than this, he could win honor while delighting you and me and himself; whereas now he will earn only shame by grieving all of us. For you will not hear things delightful to be heard; and I will discuss things vexatious to me; and he will perhaps find what he does not seek, since, while he thinks to secure an opportunity for discussion with me, he casts away every topic on which we might talk, I shall not say without awkwardness, but in any manner at all. When the things which it will behoove me to say have made him realize how great an error he has made in thinking that I erred, if he has not forsaken all shamefastness, he will cease to take up arms against the truth; and though he still desire it, he will be unable to do so when none of them remain to grasp."

"Armed or unarmed," replied Gismondo, "in any case I can take care of you this time, my Perottino. But you are too credulous if you believe I have no arms to grasp, for almost anything I can grasp is bound to be a weapon against you. Arm yourself, however; I'd hardly think of it as victory if you were not well armed when I defeated you."

The ladies laughed at the brave words of two cavaliers eager for battle. But Lisa (for so I am minded to call one of the other young women), seeing that Lavinello by his silence shunned the opportunity to speak, smiled on him and said, "Lavinello, it will be a reproach to you if while your friends are struggling, you stand there with your hands in your belt. You too should join the fray."

"But, Lisa," the young man cheerfully replied, "I cannot join the fray without falling into reproach; for when, as you see, my friends are engaged in struggling together, it would not be honorable for me, by siding with one of them, to force the other to fight it out alone with two assailants."

"That's no excuse, Lavinello," answered the ladies as with one voice. Then, the other two having shown that they left the reply to her, Lisa continued, "This is no valid defense of yours for not taking up arms. These are not contentions of the kind in which, as you say, a man must take care that two are not pitted against one; in such a battle as this no one dies. Enter it then, and choose whichever side you wish."

"Lisa, Lisa, you are quite wrong," Lavinello answered, playfully shaking his finger at her; and turning to the other two, he said, "Ladies, only a moment ago I congratulated myself, believing, because I saw you intent on the scuffle between my friends, that you would not notice me or commission me to intervene in it. Now, however, since Lisa is not contented to leave me in peace, so that my friends may at least not suffer at my hands, let us allow them to fight by themselves, in their own way; and then, when they have finished their contest, picking up the weapons they have dropped, like a good fencer who keeps for himself the final thrust, I shall have an opportunity to satisfy your wishes."

After they had spoken and replied as they pleased and all had remained silent for a little, Perottino, rousing himself from the depths of thought and raising his face toward the ladies, proceeded: "Now let Gismondo know what is coming to him; and since he has broken this dike, let him not repent if he may perhaps have more water on his hands than necessary and it shall otherwise befall than he has thought. Ladies, I cannot expect to describe for you, in any manner suitable to such a subject, this universal plague, this general outrage against mankind, called love—not that I, who am alone and weak, might ever describe it, but that all the readiest, most expert orators would not suffice to do it justice. Yet that little which I shall say of it, for I do have something to say on the subject, will perhaps seem too much to Gismondo, who misrepresents the truth to himself; but to you who are young it may still, in future years, serve as a warning to be told, in some wise, the manner of this savage beast."

When he had spoken, Perottino fell silent and then, in a somewhat more even voice, began his argument as follows: "Love is not the son of Venus, my worthy ladies, though he is so designated in the poets' fables, who, nevertheless differing among themselves in this very lie, make him the son of diverse goddesses, as if anyone could have various mothers; yet he, begotten not by Mars or Mercury or Vulcan either, or any other god, but in our minds by those base progenitors, the excessive lust and heavy indolence of men, is born the offspring of our sensuality and vice. At that moment our minds embrace the child and, swaddling him with tenderest hopes, provide the nourishment of vain, besotted thoughts, a milk which flows more freely the more the thirsty infant sucks, so that in short order he grows too big for all his garments. Like any newborn babe he appears charming and pretty to his nurses and holds them spellbound at first sight; in most cases, however, he alters day by day and, ever changing, ever varying, in a short time assumes new forms and another style, so that soon he no longer appears as he once did at birth. But whatever his appearance, he is no other, both in himself and in his actions, than a kind of venom; and from that word, I take it, whoever first derived them shrewdly formed the terms *Venus* and *venery* to designate Love's work, perhaps in order that men might elude him when they read his character inscribed upon the very forehead of his deeds.

"And in truth, all who follow him receive no better guerdon for their toils than bitterness and earn no other prize, no other recompense than grief; for that is the coin in which he pays his servants. He always has an infinite number of them and leads many of his treasurers with him to deal his bounty out in fullest measure, bestowing most on those who have most generously bestowed themselves and all their liberty upon that treacherous lord. Wherefore men ought not to complain if while they are in love, they are forever gulping down a thousand bitter drafts and every day feel torments without number; for this is their customary life, nor can it be otherwise, and the only thing of which they ought or can justly complain is that they are in love. Thus, it is not possible to love without bitterness, nor does anyone ever feel or suffer bitterness in any way except through love."

When Perottino had spoken to this effect, Madame Berenice, who had listened most attentively, interposed, "You know already, Perottino, what you have to do. Therefore, besides encouraging Gismondo to answer your arguments in full, as he lately promised us, you will not perhaps deny, even to one of us women, the opportunity to refute the ugly things you say. Then, if we are permitted to intervene in your debate, in which I for one would not like to make any misstep or to have you consider me disrespectful or presumptuous—"

"Madame," Gismondo broke in, "we could never hold you disrespectful or presumptuous because you spoke or reasoned, nor your companions either, since we all came here to do precisely that. So let each of you intervene as often as you please; these discussions are no more ours than yours."

"Then," said Madame Berenice, "I shall feel free to blaze a trail for my companions"; and turning again to Perottino, she went on, "Indeed, if you had said only that one could not love without bitterness, I would have remained silent, nor would I have dared to speak before Gismondo. But to add that bitterness cannot be felt in any other way than through love seems excessive to me, not to say indecent; for, unless I mistook your meaning, you implied that there is no grief which is not caused by love."

"Nay, madame, you have understood me very well," replied Perottino; "and I say exactly what you report, that there is no condition of grief, no kind of sorrow in the lives of men which is not caused by love and does not derive from it as a rivulet from a fountain. The very nature of things, if we consider it, will quickly make this clear. For, as we each should know, all the good and all the evil things which can somehow bring delight or grief to men are of three kinds and no more,—of mind, of fortune, and of body; and since no grief can come of things which are good, let us discuss the three kinds of evils by which it is produced.

"Heavy fevers, unwonted poverty, our wickedness and

· 22 ·

ignorance, and the infinite army of all other mischiefs which are like these, undoubtedly bring us grief, more or less serious according to their condition and to ours,—grief which would not befall us if we had not loved their opposites. For if the body suffers when tormented by some disease, it is only because it has a natural affection for its health, which if it did not of its very nature love, it could feel no more pain than does dry wood or solid rock. And if we fret ourselves when fortune has brought us down from high to low estate, it is due to the love of riches, of honors, and of other similar things which attaches itself to them through long use or unwise choice. Thus, if there is anyone who does not love them, as we read of that philosopher who at the capture of his city sought to keep nothing for himself, being contented with no more than what he always carried,—he surely does not suffer from the bitter jests of fortune.

"Likewise, the fair virtue and useful understanding which harbor in our minds are wont to be loved through natural instinct and to be desired because every man, when he sees that he has acted on some hidden motive of vice or ignorance, is vexed as with a grievous circumstance. And even though some fellow could be found who in his vicious and unenlightened living would not somehow at times be saddened by his evil ways, there is no doubt that only his extreme ignorance and unlimited obstinacy in pursuing the former would explain his failure to hold virtue and understanding in some way dear. Nor does this happen to men alone, for it manifestly appears among the beasts, who in general have a warm affection for their offspring newly born, while they still remain in their care; if one of them dies or is taken from them at that time, they grieve as if they had human knowledge. But those same beasts are in no wise disquieted to see their children, when full-grown and able to take care of themselves, throttled and torn to pieces before their very eyes; and why? because they no longer love them.

"Therefore it should be clear to you that, as every stream arises from some spring, so every sorrow derives from some love; and just as there is no stream without its spring, so it must be true, as you understood me to say, that there is no grief without some love. And since, as I said, bitterness is none other than the grief which the mind suffers through some occasion, I reaffirm the same conclusion which you, madame, have already refused to admit, namely that men do not feel or endure bitterness for any other cause than love."

While Madame Berenice was silently considering these words, which had caught her off guard, Gismondo smiled and said, "This afternoon, to be sure, you would easily distemper all the sweetness of love with the bitterness of your argument alone, my Perottino, if we should grant your argument. But I think otherwise; and when I have more time to answer you, we shall have a better chance to see if this great bitterness of yours cannot be made sweet again. Meanwhile show us how much truth there is in that other proposition, that no one can love without bitterness."

"To that I was coming even now," replied Perottino; "and it would take only a few words, Gismondo, to show you my reasons for believing that each of us proves it in his own experience. But since you have insisted on involving me in these arguments, I'm of a mind to search them more widely.

"Surely then, ladies, there is no perturbation of the soul so wearisome, so heavy, so impetuous and violent, nor one which so spins and dashes us, as that which we name love. Writers call it sometimes fire because, just as fire consumes the things on which it seizes, so love consumes us and destroys; sometimes madness because the lover resembles those whom the Furies lash, Orestes, Ajax, and others of whom we read. And having learned through long experience that there is no more certain infelicity or woe than love, on lovers they have conferred these two epithets as their peculiar property, with the result that in every book, on every leaf the phrases *woeful lover* and *unhappy lover* have been written. No one, it is certain, calls Love charming; no one ever describes him as sweet or humane; all literature reveals him to be cruel, tart, and proud. Read what thousands have had to say of him, and in all of them you will find little or nothing but sorrow. In some the verses breathe out sighs, and whole books by many poets weep; the rhymes, the ink, the sheets, the very volumes are on fire. Suspicions, injuries, estrangements, wars are told in every song which treats of Love, and these are only his less telling blows. Despairs, rebellions, vengeances, chains and stabs and deaths,—who can run over them without feeling sorrow or shedding tears? And not only the light and popular fables of the poets, nor yet those which they more wisely wrote for the instruction of our lives, but even the most serious histories and dusty annals are spotted with these deeds of love. Not to speak of the unfortunate liaison of Pyramus and Thisbe; of the unbridled, illicit passion of Myrrha and Byblis; of the long-standing guilt of Medea; and of the tragic exits made by all of them, which, granting that they did not actually occur, yet were invented by the ancients to teach us that actual love affairs may have such terminations:—there can be no doubt that in the midst of their endearments Paolo and Francesca fell dead together, both transfixed by the same steel knife as by their single love. Neither do writers feign the story of Tarquin, whom so strong a passion for Lucretia overcame that it caused his exile and at the same time the loss of his kingdom, as well as in the end his death. And everybody believes that a man of Troy and a Greek woman set all Europe and Asia on fire with their love. But I pass over a thousand similar examples which each of you must frequently have read in new as well as older books.

"Thus it is manifest that Love procures not only sighs and tears, not merely individual deaths, but even the ruin of ancient seats, of mighty cities, and of whole provinces besides. Such are his measures, ladies; such memories of himself he leaves; and whoever writes of him must deal with them. Take care then, Gismondo, lest, if you would demonstrate that Love is good, you may not be compelled to go into the thousands of ancient and modern writers who speak of him as an abomination."

When Perottino had finished, Lisa, who while she listened had been lying on her left side with her arm upon the rim of the fountain and her hand at her throat, sat up and said, "Whatever objections Gismondo may have to make, let him look to his answer when he pleases or when it is time. But now answer me, Perottino: if Love causes as many evils as you say our writers hold against him, why do they treat him as a god? For, as I have often read, they make men worship him and consecrate altars to him and offer vows to him and give him wings with which to flit through heaven. Whoever does evil is certainly not a god, and whoever is a god surely does not do evil. Therefore, please tell me how this may be. And in doing so you will perhaps please Madame Berenice and Sabinetta no less than me; for they too must have entertained this doubt earlier in the discussion, as I did, though I never found so good an opportunity as now to ask about it."

When the other two ladies had also spoken and showed that it would be equally pleasant to them to hear Perottino's explanation, after a moment's silence he replied: "Poets, Lisa, who were the first teachers of conduct at a time when rough and savage men were not yet well banded in societies, were instructed by nature, which had given them powers of expression and of mind fit for the task, to find verses with whose sound they might soften the brutality of those who, having come forth from trees and caves without other knowledge of themselves, still lived like beasts; and scarcely had these first teachers uttered their songs when, wherever they went singing, they began to lead the savage men who were enchanted by their voices. The charming lyre of Orpheus, which drew the animals enraptured from their dens, the lofty tree trunks from their groves, and from their mountains heavy rocks, and headlong rivers from their courses, was only the voice of one of these first singers, which those men who had been dwelling with the brutes among the trees, in forests and on mountains and along the banks of rivers, followed. But when that lewd race had been gathered in this way, they must be taught how to live and shown the true quality of things, so that by pursuing virtuous courses they might be drawn from evil ones; and since the grandeur of nature could not enter those narrow souls nor reason penetrate their lazy minds to speak to them, the poets yet devised these fables, in which, as under a transparent glass, they veiled the truth. Thus, forever delighting them with the novelty of their lies and among these occasionally discovering to them the truth, now with one fable, now with another, they little by little taught them a better way of life. So, while the world was still young and its people almost unmastered, Love, together with many other forces, was made a deity, as you have called him, Lisa, for no other reason than to show that brutal race, under the name of *god*, what power this passion wielded over human minds.

"Indeed, if we wish to consider the power Love has over us and our whole lives, it will be clearly seen that infinite and truly marvelous, and a sufficient justification for making him a god, as I have said, are the miracles he works to our most deadly harm. For one man lives in fire like a salamander; another, having lost all vital heat, grows as cold as ice; another melts like snow in sunlight; a fourth, with no more sense or feeling than the rocks, stays mute and motionless. One lives without his heart, having given it to a lady who tears it in a thousand pieces every hour; one changes now into a fountain, now a tree, now a wild animal; one whom violent words have borne above the clouds may fall at any moment; and one dwells at the center of the earth and in the deep abyss. And now if you were to ask me how I know all this without having read about it, I'd say that I know it all by proof and speak of what experience taught.

"Furthermore, it is marvelous to think how many and how bitter are the inequalities, the dissensions, the delusions which Love pours and mixes in his servants' minds with such painful incongruity. For who will not agree that they are wretched beyond all other misery when they touch the extremes of joy and sorrow at the same time and when, as it often happens, they mingle bitter tears with sweetest laughter? or when they desire and dread at the same moment, so that, filled with the heat and fire of their great longing, they grow pale, and yet they tremble in their icy fear? or when they are overcome by opposite afflictions, and pride and humility, impatience and misgiving, war and peace all equally assail them at one time? or when their tongues are silent, but their faces speak and hearts cry out, they hope and they despair, and they embrace both life and death together? or when, through ever entertaining contrary emotions, as they are not wont to do in other things, and through being torn by them in the same instant both here and there, amid all these and similar excesses they lose both head and heart? Surely these lovers should convince us that what some philosopher once said is true: that every man has two souls, with one of which he wishes in one way and with the other in another, since it does not seem possible that a single soul could wish two things which are opposed.

"Though all these miracles are brought to pass by Love in his campaigns, yet the last of which I spoke happens more frequently than any other; and amid the dissonance of countless sorrows, this, like a string well-tuned, responds more often to the tone of truth, being the one which best accords with lovers' hearts, that is, the grief which makes them seek to live and yet embrace their death. For while they go in search of pleasure and believe that they are following it, they are hot in the pursuit of their affliction, enchanted by what seems to be good fortune; and in the end, through suffering a thousand new, excruciating torments, they all, in one way or another, procure themselves a wretched, foolish death. And who will deny that everyone whom mere love-folly so lightly tumbles to destruction dies foolishly and wretchedly? None surely but the victims, who often, what with extremity of grief and lack of good advice, find life so oppressive that they not only hold it of little value but willingly assail it, some because they feel that in this way they can end their sorrows more speedily than in any other, and some to make their ladies' eyes show pity once, happy if they can draw a pair of tears in recompense of all their woes.

"A novel lunacy, does it not seem to you, my ladies, that lovers seek to end their lives for such slight, eccentric causes? So it seems, but it is true; for some time ago, and not only once, I felt that death, if it were granted me, would be a blessing (and indeed it would be a blessing still, now more than ever). Thus lovers struggle against the course of nature, which stimulates all men to

love themselves and take continual precautions to preserve their lives; while these, who since they love another, have grown to hate themselves, not only take no
care to preserve their lives, but often, out of self-ferocity,
will voluntarily reject them in their scorn.

"Someone may say, however, 'Perottino, these fables
are more suitable for amorous disputation than rational
argument. For if you were as eager to perish as you say,
who could have prevented you? Every living man has
it in his power to die, just as those already dead do not
have it in their power to come alive again.' But the folly
of these words is made evident by the difficulty of the
deed.

"Ladies, you may well wonder at what I am about
to say; for if I had not learned it of my own experience,
I would hardly have dared to imagine, much less relate
it. Unlike all other kinds of men, lovers do not feel the
last bitterness of death; nay, death is often in a manner
denied to them since, as we know, one who is in extreme
misery may be quite happy to die. It often happens,
therefore, although you may never have heard of it and
may not believe it possible, that when these lovers whom
their long agony has overcome are near to death and
already feel life withdrawing from their troubled hearts,
the wretches take such ecstasy and joy in dying that this
pleasure, which comforts their poor souls all the more
because they are so unaccustomed to all pleasure, restores
their weakened spirits and sustains the life which was
about to fail. And however incredible this experience
may appear, I can cite my own case as evidence that it

can occur to one in love, and show, by way of substantiation, certain verses I once made to describe it, though it is much more suitable for me to weep than sing."

Here, as if overtaken by some sharp desire, Madame Berenice suddenly broke forth with this reflection: "Ah, Perottino, may that god of whom you speak crown all your days with joy if, before you continue your discourse, you will recite these verses. For a long time I have been exceedingly curious to hear one of your songs, and I am sure that it would likewise please these other ladies who are listening to you, no less than me; for we know very well how much your rhymes are prized by young men who are experts."

Then Perottino, allowing a deep sigh to escape with his words, replied: "That god with whom it is my misfortune to have grown only too familiar, madame, can hardly crown my days with joy, nor would he ever do so though he could make all other men rejoice, as he cannot. For my deceitful fortune has deprived me of that boon, so that nothing can, or will ever, be either glad or dear to me except the end of all things; and though I often summon death, my lot forbids that it should harken, perhaps in order that I may remain alive as an example of long-enduring misery.

"Now I have undertaken to obey you and revealed what I might better have kept hidden (for a man is wiser on the whole to die in silence than in lamentation); and even though my rhymes are hardly fit to be revealed to gay and sportive ladies, I shall venture it." Then, while his last words moved the young women's pliant hearts to pity, Perottino, who only with considerable effort restrained his tears, having recovered himself, began to speak these verses:

When, Love, I apprehend
  How heavily you rack and choke my breath,
  Headlong I rush on death,
  Hoping to bring my torments to an end.
But when I reach the bay
  Which wafts me into port from seas of grief,
  I feel such sweet relief
  My soul revives and I am forced to stay.
So living digs my grave;
  So dying raises me again to life.
  O misery too rife,
  Which, wrought by one, the other cannot stave.

The ladies and the other young men were commending Perottino's song when he interrupted them, shunning their praises and wishing to return to his first deliberations; but Madame Berenice seized the opportunity to say, "Though, contrary to all other men, you take commendation ill, be at least contented, when you have recalled some of your verses in the course of so thoughtful a discussion, to reveal them. For all three of us desire to do you honor; and the same is true of your companions, whom, as I am sure they love you with brotherly affection, you will vastly delight with a little labor, no matter how many times they have already heard your verses."

To these words Perottino replied that he would do what he could and then resumed: "What more can one say in the matter, except that the fate of lovers is so pre-eminently wretched that being alive, they cannot live, and dying, cannot die? Indeed, the only motive which spurs me on to speak of love's strange bitterness is that you young ladies, whose good is ever dear to me, may be satisfied to know its acrid flavor by having it discussed rather than by tasting it yourselves.

"But mark the puissance of this god, which I know not whether to call more harmful or more marvelous; for Love neither wishes nor is satisfied by this approbation of his miracles. Although it may be argued that the agony which lovers feel in living can bring them to their death and the joy which they feel in dying can bring them to life, Love sometimes will not only prevent one of them from dying who has no reason to live, but make him live by fiercely assailing him with two obvious forms of death, as it were two lives. Ladies, what I am saying seems even to me to be immeasurably strange, and yet it is surely true; if it were not, I would now be free of countless other sorrows in which I am enmeshed. For Love having thrust my tortured heart betimes into the hottest fire, in which it was inevitable that I should die since my own powers were unable to resist such heat, the cruelty of that very lady with love of whom I burned made me fall to weeping so plentifully that my blazing heart was steeped in tears and by their help recovered from its flames; and yet these tears would of themselves have so relaxed the tendons of my life and made so deep a pool within my heart that I would have surely died, had it not been that everything my weeping softened, the arid flames made hard again and so restored me. Thus, since both these mischiefs came to my assistance and life returned when their deadly perils overcame each other, my heart remained alive. But how alive, you see; for I cannot conceive an existence more wretched than that of one who lives only because he is assailed on either hand by death and indeed actually dies twice over.

At this point Perottino fell silent for a moment; but when he would have passed on to something else, Gismondo, stopping him by holding an open hand toward him, remarked to Madame Berenice, "He doesn't keep the promise he made to you a moment ago, that whenever he could, he would let you hear his rhymes. For he has already made a charming song on the very miracle he has just described, and yet he does not say it to you. Make him say it since it will really please you."

As soon as the lady heard this, she broke out, "So, Perottino, you already fail your compact? We thought you were a man of your word." And after all the ladies had bidden him, with these and other phrases, to tell them not only the song Gismondo had mentioned but others too, if they came pat, and had made him promise more than once to do so, he finally began the recitation in a voice which would move stones:

Lady, you've set me all
    Afire, to make me die before my day;
    And then as if this outrage seemed too small,
    You've made me weep to double my decay.
    Now I would humbly pray,
    Take one offence away
    Since I have not two lives for you to slay.

For still that fire is quenched
　　By every tear that for your sake descends;
　　And still my heart, that sorrow would have drenched,
　　The very flame which dries, in turn defends.
　　So, as one evil spends,
　　The other yet amends,
　　And I draw benefit from what offends.
If you such sport derive
　　From seeing this burnt ember decompose,
　　Which spite of you and me is still alive,
　　Why not a kinder heart for once disclose?
　　Your zeal without repose
　　Can only dull your blows
　　And thus prolong a life replete of woes.
Yet, lady, I'm not grieving
　　At you so much as Love, who gives you head,—
　　Nay, at myself, myself not yet relieving.
　　But what can I? Those holding Love in dread
　　By crooked laws are led;
　　For who has ever read
　　A man must stay alive when he's twice dead?

His song completed, he continued: "Does it not seem
fitting to you, Lisa, that the worker of these miracles
should be called a god? Does it not seem that those first
men had good reason to give him such a name? For all
things that occur outside of nature's wonted course are
called miracles because they make men marvel; and
whether heard or seen, they can only proceed from
some supernatural cause, such as God above all others.

This name they therefore gave to Love as to one whose power they thought extended beyond nature's.

"Now in my eagerness to show you rather my own than others' sufferings, I have still not revealed to you more than the least part of my infinite torments; and yet, though they were no more numerous than those you have heard, they might, by the overwhelming example of my misery, persuade the world how powerful this god is; but all of them together may be counted little or nothing in comparison with those torments which other men endure. If I had wished to describe and discuss the stories we may read about a hundred thousand lovers, just as in churches the faith which not one but infinite numbers feel toward a god is set forth in a thousand votive paintings,—you would surely have marveled at them as shepherds do when, having for the first time been brought to the city on some necessary business, they see a thousand things at once which fill them with a boundless admiration. Nor because I believe my woes are heavy, as they indeed are, would it be right to say that those of other men are light, or that Love does not perhaps fall upon a thousand other hearts as violently as he has done on mine, or that he does not beget in them miracles as many and as strange as those which he begot in me. Nay, I am convinced that, thanks to my master, I have many fellows in this trial, though not all of them are so easily recognized and known as I have known myself.

"But along with their other misapprehensions lovers nourish this, that each believes himself to be the most wretched of his kind and enjoys that distinction, as if he had received a victor's crown, nor can allow that any other should be brought by love to such a depth of suffering as he himself has reached. Indeed, if we may believe the reports of antiquity, Argia loved exceedingly; and whoever had heard her weep, as we must think she did when she threw herself upon the wounds of her dead husband, would know that she found her own sorrow greater than that of any other woman. Nevertheless, we read that Evadne, who felt the same kind of grief at the same time as she, not only mourned for her dead husband, but with a lofty contempt for her own life followed him. So did Laodamia after the death of hers; so Panthea, the fair Asian queen; so that unhappy girl of Sestos for her lover; so many others likewise. For every condition of unhappiness, we may believe, resembles many others of that kind, though they are not easy to detect since misery will often seek to hide itself.

"Then, Lisa, if you will add the torments of other men to mine, as far as you feel you can, without my going into all the stories, you should be able to infer that the power of your god extends as far beyond what my example has revealed as there are those whose love resembles mine; and they are surely countless. For to Love, who can do what he alone desires, instantaneously and everywhere, it means nothing that by putting a thousand lovers to the proof with his mighty deeds, he risks the loss of all their lives. So he has his fun; and though it causes us an infinity of tears and torments, he makes our grief the subject of his jokes and laughter. And now the vampire grows, as it were, accustomed to our blood and fond of our wounds, so that the rarest of all his miracles is making someone fall in love who hardly feels his grief. Few, therefore, are those lovers (and I do not know if there is even one of them) who can preserve a mean in their afflictions, while we see the contrary all the time. Not to mention that Love frequently converts us calm, attentive, studious, philosophical souls into dangerous prowlers of the night, bearers of weapons, vaulters over walls, nay even stabbers of our fellow men: every day we see a thousand, and those perhaps who are held to be the most trustworthy and the wisest, who when they turn to love, go plainly mad.

"But when men had made Love a god on the grounds which you, Lisa, have just heard, they thought it fitting to give him a certain form, in order that he might be more completely known. Therefore they drew him naked to show not only that lovers have nothing of their own, because they themselves are the possessions of another, but also that by despoiling themselves of judgment, they become naked of all reason. They painted him as a boy, not that one born together with the first of men is really a child, but because he makes those who follow him become children in their powers, as if some new Medea with her strange potions made babies out of white-haired patriarchs. They gave him wings because lovers, who are lifted on the pinions of their mad desires, flit lightly through the empty air, even, their hopes make them believe, right up to heaven. Furthermore, men gave him a burning torch to grasp because, just as the brightness of a fire pleases, but its burning grieves, so Love, which seems to be a pleasant thing, delights us at first sight, but when we understand it by experience, grows immeasurably harsh; which were it known before he burnt us, how much narrower would the kingdom of this tyrant be to-day and how much less the crowd of lovers! Yet we, being enamored of our own undoing, troop joyfully to the flame like butterflies; nay, frequently we even set fire to ourselves, and then, like Perillus in the bull which he devised, we clearly see ourselves consumed by the very flames we lighted. But to complete the portrait of this evil god which men have painted with the various colors of their misery: to all these things which I have told you, Lisa, they add his bow and arrows to signify that Love inflicts such wounds on us as some skillful archer might; yet these are all the more deadly that he gives them in the heart, and have this added disadvantage, that he never grows weary or is moved by pity when he sees our powers failing; nay, he only deals his blows the faster, the more he feels that we grow weaker.

"Now, Lisa, I believe that I have clearly shown you what reasons induced men to call that one a god whom we call Love and why they so depicted him, as you have seen. But if he is studied with a careful eye, he is actually found to be no god, which it would be a wicked thing to think he was and a grave error to believe; nay, it is certain that he is only what we ourselves would wish. For love must of necessity be sown in the ground of our desires, without which it would no more exist than a plant without its earth. Indeed, when we receive it in our minds, we usually give it a foothold and allow it to take root in our wills; then it grows so strong of itself that in spite of us it remains there, pricking our hearts with thorns and working its strange wonders, as everyone who proves them knows.

"But since I have gone a good way in my argument with you, it is time to return to Gismondo, whom I left at the very outset, when you called me aside, just after he had asked how it might be true, as I had said, that one could not love without bitterness. Now anyone who did not perhaps wish to injure himself by arguing against the truth would surely be able to understand this from the evidence just cited; but so that more profit may accrue to you ladies, who, being women and so with less experience of fortune than we have, have greater need to be advised, and because, now that I have begun, it will comfort me to speak of my sufferings at greater length, as often happens to the wretched,—I shall continue to speak of this. Thus I shall at the same time oblige and disoblige you with my counsel, discoursing and informing you of things which can cause much unhappiness to those who do not understand them."

Perottino had fallen silent while he prepared to speak again, when Gismondo, who was studying the shadows, now grown somewhat longer, turned to his fair companions and said, "Dear ladies, I have always heard that the hardier one's foe, the higher is one's victory; so the more Perottino strengthens his arguments and the longer he spends himself on his bad cause, sharpening his pointed speech, the worthier the garland he is weaving for my brows. But I fear that I may not have time enough to answer him if we, as usual, wish to join the others in the palace at the hour of festivity; for the sun already bows toward evening, and the space that we have yet to linger here is scarcely more than that now passed. Time is so fleeting and Perottino's charming words have so engaged our minds that it seems hardly a moment since we came."

Sabinetta, the youngest of the three ladies, who at the beginning of these discussions had seated herself on the grass under the laurels, withdrawing from the others, as it were, to listen, had not spoken a word since Perottino had begun. But now she said, rather unwillingly than not, "It would do an injury to Perottino if you wished, Gismondo, that he should be compelled to cut short his discourse. Today let him speak without restraint and as long as he pleases, and then tomorrow you can reply to him; for it will be more pleasant if we can divert ourselves in this way again, having other days to spend here, and you will find it easier to reply when you have had the intervening time to think things over."

Since Sabinetta's suggestion pleased everyone, it was decided that they would return to the same place the next day. Then, when all the others were silent, Perottino began: "Just as their ports spell peace to ships that wander in distress, or their native woods to hunted creatures, so true conclusions are the goal of doubtful arguments; and when these are lacking, it does not help to muster and compile a heap of fine declamatory phrases, perhaps more diligently sought the further they depart from truth, in order to stuff the minds of listeners who scrutinize not only the forehead and face of words, but their breast and heart as well. And tomorrow, ladies, I apprehend that this will happen to Gismondo, who, when he hopes to win the garland in this contest, relies on his own wit rather than giving thought to yours or considering the weakness of his cause. Fortune, indeed, would favor his expectations, since it allows him a longer space to prepare his reply than I have to bring forth my arguments, were he not the enemy of truth.

"And that he may not later accuse me of the fault I now impute to him, in answer to his question I say that whenever a man does not possess what he wishes, he submits to sufferings which disquiet all his peace, as if it were a city which its foes assailed, and hold him in continual torment, more or less serious according to the gravity of his desires. By possession I do not mean ownership of horses or clothes or houses, the master of which is called their possessor although he does not use them exclusively or always or according to his wish; by possession I mean the complete enjoyment of what one loves and enjoyment in that way which is most agreeable to him. But since this is quite obvious of itself, there is no need for me to discuss it further.

"Now I would like you to tell me, Gismondo, if you believe that the man who loves another can ever completely enjoy the one he loves. If you say yes, you are in manifest error because a man cannot completely enjoy what is not wholly part of himself; for external things are always subject to fortune and to chance, and not to us, while the very word *another* betrays that its subject is external. If you say no, Gismondo, then you must confess (nor can lovers defend you) that whoever loves feels and sustains affliction at all hours. And since the bitterness of the mind is only that venom with which the feelings poison it, it is, of necessity, no more possible that Venus should be without venom than that water should dry, or fire wash, or snow burn, or the sun fail to give light. Now do you see, Gismondo, what brief and simple words contain the unadulterated truth? But why do I argue a truth which the very hand can touch? Do I say, 'The hand'? Nay, even the heart. Nor is there anything which makes itself felt more inwardly, or transfixes the soul by piercing us more deeply to the marrow, than love does, which like a powerful venom shoots its vigor to the heart and like a skillful highwayman would set his hand at once upon the jewel of men's lives.

"So, leaving syllogisms to Gismondo, to whom, as to their peculiar champion, they are more suitable than to you ladies harkening our debate, I shall discuss the problem with you more openly and in this way. Running over the various passions of the soul will make it clearer that its bitterness is something derived from their stinging taste; and since we have already begun to speak of them and you have granted me the right to talk today, a right which you had given a little earlier to Gismondo, I shall continue to discuss them, weaving a longer fabric from their strands.

"Now, ladies, the chief passions of the mind, from which all the others are derived and to which they return, are three and no more: excessive desire, excessive joy, and excessive fear, whether of future misery or present woe. Since these passions, like winds which are opposed to one another, disturb the mind's tranquillity and all the ordered quiet of our lives, writers have more exactly named them *perturbations*. Although the first of these perturbations is that proper to Love, who is nothing but desire, yet he, not being contented with his limits, leaps over into others'

· 44 ·

houses and, blowing on his torch, sets all of them aflame. That fire, having consumed our minds, will often set a period to our lives; and even when this does not occur, it will not fail to bring us to a life which is more odious than death.

"To begin, then, with this desire, I say it is the fountainhead of all the other passions and that all our ills spring from it as trees do from their roots. For whenever the love of something is lighted in us, it straight impels us to follow and seek for that thing; and while we do so, it leads us headlong into perilous disorders and a thousand miseries. It drives a brother to covet the unnatural embraces of a sister for whom he feels an evil love, a stepmother to covet those of a stepson, and sometimes (what I shudder to say) a father to covet those of a virgin daughter: things rather monstrous than bestial, which it is much better to pass over in silence than to describe. So, leaving them in their unspeakable disgrace and turning to our own affairs, I tell you that this desire rules and guides and drives our thoughts, our steps, and all our days to endings sad and unforeseen. Nor are we often aided by those who use reason to oppose our love, for though we see that we are bound for ruin, yet we do not know how to save ourselves; or even if we once succeed in holding fast, we give way again like those who only grow the sicker for returning to their vomit. Thus it happens that as the sun, on which we gazed when it arose this morning, at midday dazzles anyone who studies it, so at first we can sometimes clearly see the nature of our newborn evil, which later, being full-grown, quite blinds the eye of reason.

"But Love is never satisfied to hold us merely by one

hook or lash us with one whip; nay, just as all the other passions are born of desires, so from the first desire which springs up in us a thousand others are derived as from a great river, and in lovers these are as various as they are numberless. For although they all, in general, tend to one conclusion, yet because their objects are diverse and diverse the fortunes of lovers, each undoubtedly desires in a different way. Some, in order that they may once reach their prey, put all their strength into one sprint; and what hardships they encounter! how many times they fall! how many tenacious thorns fray their miserable soles! and frequently they are winded before the game is caught. Others, who have won what they love, desire only to maintain that happy state and, devoting every thought and act, at every moment, to that one end, are wretched in their joy, poor in their opulence, and bankrupt in their good fortune. Still others, having lost their goods, seek to repossess them; and under a thousand harsh conditions, a thousand evil stipulations, consuming themselves in prayers, in tears, in shrieks, while they contend for what is lost, they madly put their lives in jeopardy.

"But these toils and cries and torments are not perceived at first; for just as at the entrance of some forest we seem to have a beaten path, but the further we penetrate, the narrower that track becomes, so when the desire for some object first arouses us, we seem to be able to attain it with the greatest ease, but the further we go, the smaller and the more difficult our road becomes at every step. And this trial serves to introduce our other griefs. In order to reach our goal, we try to remove every obstacle that hinders us; and what cannot be gained by open means must be obtained by devious. Hence anger, injuries, and litigations arise, and all too soon that evil follows which no one would have thought possible in the beginning. Not to describe every minute circumstance: how often has some lover desired the death of countless men, and sometimes perhaps those dearest to him? How many women have been led by their unbridled appetites to dig their husbands' graves? Believe me, ladies, if I thought one could say worse than this, I would say nothing more. But what more can be said? that a married couple's sacred bed, which knew the most secret portion of their lives and saw their tenderest embraces, should for some rash new love be painted with the sinless blood of one, shed by the other's guilty blade? Nay, let us stand off from desire's ugly cliffs and sail across the turbid seas of counterfeit delight.

"It must be obvious to you, my ladies, that every joy expands as the desire grows within our minds for that which causes joy, and that the more immoderately we have first pursued the things which we desire, the more acutely we rejoice in their pursuit. And inasmuch as no appetite has so much power over us, nor carries us so forcefully toward the object it desires, as that which Love spurs and scourges with his whip, it follows that no joy passes so far beyond all reason as that of lovers when they achieve something which they desire. Indeed, who would derive such pleasure from one little glance, or who would place his utmost happiness in two fragmentary words, or one brief handshake, or some other trifle of the kind, except a lover, who is so irrationally eager for these very bagatelles? Surely no one, I believe. Nor is it therefore right to say that in this respect lovers are better off than all other men; for it is clear that each of their joys is as a rule, or rather always, attended by a myriad of sorrows, so that they, as others are not wont, for every satisfaction pay a thousand times with grief.

"No delight which goes beyond wise limits is healthy, and it may rather be called a fatuous illusion than a true delight. Moreover, it is injurious to lovers because it leaves them tipsy with its poison; for as if they had submerged their memories in Lethe, forgetting everything but their own harm and laying aside every virtuous activity, every praiseworthy discipline, every honorable undertaking, every duty, to their disgrace they concentrate their thoughts on this delight alone. As a result they not only procure their shame and ruin, but also become their own antagonists and voluntarily enslave themselves to countless sorrows. How many nights does the unhappy lover pass in wakeful misery, how many days does he waste in thinking one assiduous thought, how many footsteps pace in vain, how many pages write with tears no less than ink, before he earns one hour of pleasure? And it may chance to bring him some displeasure since it is often mingled with grievous words, hot sighs, and actual tears, not perhaps without some danger to his person, or if none of these befalls him, still with a certain twinge of heart that an hour so fleeting bears away those pleasures he toiled so many seasons to acquire. Who does not know how many regrets, insults, alterations, griefs, and vengeful thoughts, and bonfires of disdain a thousand times consume and reconsume the lover before he gleans one satisfaction? Who does not know with how many jealousies, suspicions, emulations, and black looks his every brief delight is bought? The sands have no more shells, the breezes flutter no more leaves in this green garden, now so fully robed, than there are woes in every holiday of love.

"And even if these same holidays were once completely free of grief and pensiveness—assuming what could never be—, then they might only be the more disastrous to us. For a lover's fortune does not always stay the same (nay, it changes more often than any other in the world since it serves a more inconstant master than the others do); and when this happens, our misery appears the heavier, the greater our felicity appeared before. Then we lament for Love; we grieve at ourselves; living becomes a burden to us, as these verses will show you from my own sad case. And if you perhaps find them longer than their wont, it suits the weight of my disasters, which could not be conveyed in fewer.

Man never had more calm and quiet days
   Than I, and never passed more tranquil nights
   Or took more pleasure in his happy state
   Than I, when I began to drive the pen
   I loved, and not with suffering or tears,
   At my first entrance on a lover's life.
Now Love has bent the pathway of my life;
   That happy time and those unclouded days
   Which never knew the bitter taste of tears
   Have faded into black, tormented nights;
   To suit my subject I have changed my pen
   And with my darker fortunes dimmed my state.
I never thought that from so high a state

A man might fall into so base a life,
Nor warp so smooth into so harsh a pen.
But no sun ushers forth such glorious days
That they have lacked as many dreary nights:
So close to laughter ever lurk our tears.
And close indeed my laughter was to tears.
If I had known, in that enraptured state
Of carefree song and in those kindly nights
Perhaps it would have put a period to my life,
Rather than linger out these cruel days
Which have so bitten both my heart and pen.
You, Love, who once gave matter to my pen
Of joy, now teach it bitterness and tears.
To what despair are sunk my sportive days?
What wind has rooted up my flowering state
And flung the anchored quiet of my life
Among the rocks that fret these weary nights?
Where are my lovely wide-awaking nights
Of long ago? And where my laughing pen
Which could rejoice the most distempered life?
Who has so quickly melted it to tears?
Would I had died when my uncankered state
In secrecy still fostered its fair days.
The sun has set on my serener days,
And doubled is the blackness of my nights,
Once brighter than another's daylight state.
Once, when I sang, a gay and happy pen
Gave forth my rhymes, now given to the tears
Which have embittered such a gracious life.
If everyone might fathom what my life
Was like before she turned my festive days,

She who alone was able, into tears,
I'd count myself requited for these nights
Without distilling sorrows from my pen;
But no such luck relieves my present state.
For that wild creature who gave my callow state
A cruel nip, and almost crushed my life,
Now flees the cry of my afflicted pen,
Nor ever, for remembrance of old days
Or by recital of these later nights,
Is moved to pity my incessant tears.
Echo alone has heard, and with my tears
Comparing now her own once hapless state,
She shares my grief on such unhappy nights.
And if one's end is patterned on his life,
A single fate joins these to future days:
My disembodied voice will be my pen.
Among you lovers once I had a pen
So sweet it mollified all others' tears,
I whose complaints none soothes these days.
No man believes while in a joyous state
That he will ever lead a dreary life
Or thinks in daytime of the coming nights.
But let who will rejoice at my sad nights:
She most of all who made me turn my pen
To harm and in such hatred hold my life
That I may never hope to dry my tears.
She knows it well, who from so glad a state
So quickly brought me to such sorry days.
Go, joyous days and dear familiar nights,
Since my fair state has plucked another pen
And on my tears alone I foster life.

· 51 ·

"You see, ladies, the port to which our happy fortune guides us. Although I would far rather die, I live, however long or short my life may be. But there have been many unable to remain alive, they found their grief so heavy after their great joy. When fortune brought Artemisia's husband to the grave, it so completely broke her happiness that she lived in tears all the remainder of her days and in the end died weeping, a thing which would never have occurred had she enjoyed her bliss in moderation. After her roving paramour Aeneas cast her off, Elissa cast herself away, a wretched suicide; yet she would not have suffered such a death had she been less fortunate in amorous pleasures. Nor would it seem so heart-rending to poor Niobe that she should lose her children, had she not placed in them her chief felicity. So it happens that if lovers set too high a value on their sorry joys, they either meet some bitter death or fall heir to everlasting grief; or if their rapture should be mingled with vexation, they suffer inevitable torment while their pleasures last and, when they go, are left with nothing but remorse. For all those undertakings, when their failure has brought us to ruin, make us repentant in the end.

"O sour sweetness! O poisoned medicine for lovers ailing! O painful joy which leaves your occupants no sweeter fruit than their remorse! O beauty which resembles airy smoke, no sooner eyed than gone and leaving only tears! O wings which bear us up to heaven, in order that when your wax is melted by the sun and you have fallen from our shoulders, we, like Icarus, may tumble in the sea! Such, ladies, are the pleasures one enjoys in love. And now let us consider what its terrors are.

"Poets, whose fables are wont to tell the truth occasionally, feign that in the shadowy abyss, among the dismal legions of the damned, there is one above whose skull a mighty rock hangs by the slenderest of threads; and while he gazes, fearing that at any moment it will fall, he undergoes continuous punishment. Such is the condition of those unhappy lovers who always think of possible calamities, as if they hung just overhead, and live in everlasting misery through fear; for with a kind of silent speech, I know not how, their sad hearts continually ply and torture them with prophecies of imminent disaster. Where is the lover who does not every moment fear his lady's scorn? or that she may give some other man her love? or that in some way, and there are always a thousand possible obstructions, access to his pleasure may be denied? Nay, I cannot believe that there is any man alive, whatever his condition, who while in love does not grow anxious and feel fear a thousand times each day.

"And do these cares then bring him other injuries than fear? Indeed they do, and not one but infinite, for this very fear becomes the root of many others. In order to repair those leaning ruins whose fall we think could pulverize our happiness, we seek to buttress their infirmity with many crooked props, such as the hurt or even death of others. When rude Aegisthus feared that his uncle's son, returning from the long-protracted war, might spoil his pleasures, he slew him. So likewise mad Orestes cut his cousin down before the altars of the gods, amid the sacrificing priests, in order to preserve the love he bore his sister. Not that I take any pleasure, ladies, in thumbing through such tragedies. Yet if I am to show you what

Love is really like, whom Gismondo praises for his virtue, I am compelled to show his deeds; and yet those my discourse leaves behind may be as many as the bubbles left by some ship which crowds its sails and scuds before the wind. But let us pass on to the grief of lovers in order to make an end of these evils.

"This grief, although rooted in desire like the other two passions we have studied, yet grows large or small as it is watered more or less abundantly at first by pleasure. There are plenty of lovers, then, who vex and rack themselves without relief whenever their ladies stab them with one sidelong glance or three ill-tempered words, not to mention the number of times the creatures wound their lovers without knowing why, merely because they wish to put them to a little torture. Some are ready to end it all since they cannot arrive at their desires. Some who arrive at them but fail of their enjoyment, to this apparent evil add their unceasing rancor, an evil which is real and serious. And many who have reached the culmination of their joy have been forever stricken by their ladies' deaths, so that wherever they turn their eyes or thoughts, they can see nothing but their cold and pallid shapes; and as winter fails to shake the leaves from all the trees, so time cannot remove the grief of all these lovers,—nay, as some plants each spring put forth new leaves above the old, so some of these add woe to woe; and the longer they outlive the women they have loved, the more they live in torment, using the very knife which wounded them to make their gashes deeper day by day. Nor shall I omit that lover who, when his lady's cruelty has cast him from the pinnacle of his delight into the depths of sorrow, plans to withdraw from the world in order to procure her pleasure and in his exile desires nothing but the opportunity to weep and be pre-eminently sad. This he wishes, on this he feeds, from this he draws his consolation, and to this he bends his steps. Neither sun nor star nor heaven is bright to him; nor fountains, nor green grass, nor flowers, nor course of babbling rivulets, nor sight of budding groves, nor air, nor coolness, no, nor any shade is sweet to him. But alone and ever deep in his own thoughts, his eyes brimming with tears, he seeks the least traveled valleys or most secluded woods, where he resolves to make life brief, at times releasing one of his embosomed sorrows in some doleful verse, or speaking to some dry tree trunk or solitary creature and comparing their estate with his, as if they understood.—Are you still burning to show us what a splendid thing love is, Gismondo? Tell us, are you all eagerness to demonstrate that love is good?

"Now then, ladies, that we have one by one examined these evils of desire, joy, anxiety, and grief, I feel that it would be well to consider them in a body and in no particular order. But before I move one way rather than another, I am struck by the novel form in which this venomous deceiver makes his first addresses to our minds, as if they promised merriment and play, not woeful tears and open peril to our lives. For it happens every hour that one small word, one smile, one glance seizes upon our spirits with a marvelous force and causes us to lay all our advantages, our honor, and our liberty in some lady's hands, although we know no more of her than that; and every day some movement, gait, or way of sitting begets the warmest feelings. Furthermore, how many times do we pass over the body's fairest parts, only to be strangely stirred by those which are the weakest? How many times do we become enamored of a little weeping? And though a smile leaves us unshaken, how many times does one teardrop force us to hasten to our ruin with impatient steps? How many have found the paleness of a sick woman the source of a more deadly pallor? How many whom no lambent eyes could ever snare in pleasant gardens, have been taken by the dull and hollow gaze of fever, which brought them to a still more dangerous distemper? How many who once pretended to be caught and stepped into the trap for fun, stayed there unwillingly when they'd been tied with that sturdy, narrow noose? How many who would have doused another's flame, themselves took fire and needed help? How many, hearing others speak of some lady far away, themselves have found a thousand torments drawing near? Ah, would that I had left this single thing unsaid!"

Scarcely had Perottino spoken when sudden tears welled from his eyes and his ready speech died on his lips. But as all were silent out of pity at this sight, he recovered himself and then resumed in a thick and broken voice: "O ladies, when this cruel, pretty lad sees our minds burning with such flames, he adds the fuel of hope and longing; and though the first of these is sometimes lacking, being that which only strange circumstances can produce, yet our desire does not therefore lessen or always disappear with hope. For not only do we in our human obstinacy like something all the more because it is denied us, but also the more Love feels our hope decrease, the more he works the bellows of desire to blow his fires up, which as they increase, augment our sorrows. These burst from our bosoms in moans and tears and wretched cries, for the most part to no purpose; and when we come to ourselves again, we feel our grief the more, the more our clamors are in vain. So, by scattering our tears, we make our flame burn strangely hotter. Then, about to slay ourselves, we call on death for aid.

"Yet even though expressing our grief in this manner does in a sense increase it and to go thus lamenting is undoubtedly a wretched thing, nevertheless the ability to express one's·grief has some value at moments of great suffering. But it is more wretched and more harmful not to be able in any way to give voice to our sorrows or tell their bitter cause when we desire and most need to tell. Then it is an immeasurably harsh and painful thing to be compelled to hide our grief under a happy face, within the heart, nor give an outlet, even through the eyes, to amorous thoughts, which being imprisoned, not only nourish but augment the flames; for the more narrowly a fire is contained, the greater is the force with which it burns. And all these accidents are as familiar to lovers as wind and rain are in the open air.

"But how can I say 'these'? for they are infinite, and each is painful in a different way. One who pursues a cruel lady with prayers and love and tears and mortal grief, amid a thousand agonizing thoughts that make his life unbearable glows with an ever greater passion. One who has become the lover of a piteous lady but is so unfortunate that he cannot reap his harvest, grows weaker and thinner the nearer that he sees her whom he loves yet is forbidden to enjoy; he feels that like another Tantalus he is wretchedly consumed among his infinite desires. Another, who is enslaved to some capricious lady, finds himself happy today, downcast tomorrow; and as sea foam, whipped up by wind and wave, floats now before, now after, so he, now high, now low, now hot, now cold, now fearing and now hopeful, having no stability in his affairs, feels and suffers every sort of punishment. Still another, who nourishes himself only on some small, blighted hope, wretchedly sustains his years in longer torment. And one who for the time believes that all else must fail before his plighted troth or happiness, will soon perceive that all a lover's faith is made of glass, and gape as if the earth had shrunk beneath his feet.

"Beside these there immediately come to mind a thousand other kinds of new, unpleasant things which rob us of all quiet, cause infinite anxieties, and bring us various torments. One weeps for some sudden illness of his lady, whose body has wretchedly molested and consumed his spirit. One who becomes aware of a new rival instantaneously grows jealous and, all on fire, afflicts himself with bitter, hostile thoughts, now accusing his adversary, now refusing to excuse his lady; nor is he pacified except when he alone is with her. One who is distraught by the recent marriage of his lady participates in her nuptial festivities no otherwise, and studies them with no more cheerful eye, than if they were her funeral rites and obsequies. Other lovers grieve all day in many ways when they have been unfortunately surprised by some sudden occasion for tears, which, if chance or resolution should remove, many other circumstances which are often more distressing will arise. Thus he who must, like Hercules, combat the ferocious Hydra would wrestle on much fairer terms than those who have to match their strength with the ferocity of love.

"And what I say of men is apt to be equally true of you young ladies; and perhaps—but do not take it amiss since though I speak with you, I'm not discussing you—perhaps I shall say much more. For of your very nature you are usually more inclined and more pliable to the assaults of love than we are, and your flames burn brighter than ours are wont to do, though many of your individual experiences make you much more acute and circumspect than we are.

"Furthermore, the first ardors, if they are felt by youthful minds, are more harmful to them, as heat is to the budding leaves; but if they are felt in maturity, they are undoubtedly more impetuous and fierce, just as the sky grows all the stormier the longer it has been serene and clear. Thus, whether we are young or getting on in years when we are taken ill of this infirmity, it brings our lives to a pretty pass, an arduous and very rude predicament. But all the maladies of Love, like those of the body, the longer they last, the less curable they become and the less can any remedy avail. For his habitual blandishments are his worst side since we thoughtlessly penetrate them further day by day, as if drawn into the labyrinth without our ball of twine, and then when we desire, are unable to return; sometimes, in fact, our disease becomes so natural to us that even if we could, we would not part from it.

"Besides all this, there are the long, offensive wranglings; the briefer agonies; the reconciliations which are never to be trusted; the perilous renewals of old loves, heavier as those who have already sweated find their second fevers more serious than the first; the bitter memory of sweet occasions which are gone, since to have once been happy is, as it were, the height of all unhappiness. But most cruel are the leave-takings, and especially those which follow some dearly wished-for night, with sighs and tears and long embraces, during which the lovers' hearts seem to be torn out by the roots and cloven down the middle in two parts. Alas, how bitter are the separations during which the lover is never seen to smile and feels no festive mirth, but with his thoughts tethered at all hours to his lady's image, as if his eyes were fixed on the North Star, passes this portion of his life in apprehension; while salty tears well endlessly around his sorrowing heart and painful sighs crowd from his lips, he goes in mind where he can never go in body and sees no object, however few he sees, which does not make him copiously weep.

"This, ladies, you may gather from my wretched case, whose life is such as my songs describe it, only much worse; and since I have gone so far beyond those others I recited, perhaps I shall not need to repent of having called to mind these two:

Now that my cruel and deceitful fate
   Has with a churlish hand quenched all my hope
   Of finding pity in her lovely eyes,
   I still drag out my days from date to date,
   From rack to rack, and down the rugged slope
   Still totter, calling death with feeble cries:

A cloud or dust that flies
Before the wind, a snowflake in the sun.
And if her face pursues my fleeing soul,
A thought like living coal
Consumes me till all other woes are none;
My eyes that once with gazing were beguiled
Now weep and only thus seem reconciled.
Now that my star no longer marks the way,
  My limbs at random, step by step, I guide
  By ragged roads, my thoughts dissolved in gall,
  And ask, filled with confusion and dismay,
  "Whence comes my grief? yet why so weary-eyed?
  What wins your hate for me, my all in all?"
  Amid these words there fall
  Such dismal showers from my heart's full store
  As might constrain the very stones to weep;
  And lest my anguish sleep
  And not, in some strange fashion, still grow more,
  No matter where I walk or cast my eye,
  I see no other than my lady nigh.
When by myself I plod afoot, but by
  Another strides my heart, whose hidden springs
  At every painful step distill a tear,
  "What am I now?" I muse. "What once was I?
  Who robs me of my dearest gem and brings
  Me where no hope of going back can cheer?
  Alas, why not die here
  Before I dwindle to a beggar's state?
  Who strips me of my happiness amain
  To make me wear my pain
  Eternally? Ah, world and hostile fate,

To which you draw me with the fell design
    That no man's life may be so harsh as mine!"
Walking where road or wandering feet ordain,
    Rather than die I would with weeping cloy
    My eyes, whose only wish is thus to pine.
    "O most unhappy lover," I complain,
    "Now have you reached the end of your brief joy
    And crossed the threshold of your long decline."
    Those eyes of hers which shine
    As if two stars had made my soul their state,
    Her face which was my sun not long ago,
    Her acts and words also,
    Which eased my breast of every other weight,
    Besiege my heart with banded thoughts so dire
    The wonder is that I should not expire.
Though still not dead, I do not stay alive:
    Nay, rather than receive what death awards,
    I live on hope and on my miseries.
    Dead to delight, in torment I survive;
    My joyless heart with grief so well accords
    That it still weeps with ever greater ease.
    It thinks and hears and sees
    Her yet who once so dearly warmed the same
    But now distills therein mere bitterness;
    Nor does my hot distress
    Of mind diminish by a single flame;
    She makes me turn and cry, "Great destiny,
    How grim a fate your malice deals to me!"
O song, the upward soaring trunk grows less,
    But not the grief which leaves me spent and stark;
    Wherefore I carve it on this other bark.

When Perottino had brought these verses to an end, he remained silent for a while; and then, with a harrowing sigh which seemed to escape from deep within his heart, convincing evidence of what he suffered, he resumed his recitation with the following:

I flee but cannot save myself by flight,
   Nor lift from my exhausted life the yoke
   I draw, no matter where I drag my feet;
   And memory, which flames without respite,
   Persuades me my old woes to reinvoke
   And summon as a witness every street.
   O Love, if you think meet,
   Then make my lady hear at least this plaint,
   And carry these last phrases to the part
   Where my aspiring heart
   Rose eager once, though fallen now and faint;
   As heavy and as harsh is this exile
   As my estate was smooth and sweet erewhile.
Hearing the wind pass over wooded hills,
   I sigh and ask that out of sympathy
   It tell the heavens all my painful stour.
   Hearing some valley fount or brook that spills
   Beside green paths, I with my eyes agree
   To furnish tears for one of greater power.
   If I take heed of flower
   Or leaf, it teaches me, "O pilgrim grave,
   The flower of your life is dead and sear";
   And yet my thoughts adhere
   To her who made me crabbèd fortune's slave.
   But still, the more with her my musings go,

The more with me goes cruel Love also.
On grass where ray of sunlight never lies
   I often seat myself, desiring most
   The shady wood's most dread seclusion.
   I fix my loving thought on those fair eyes
   Which made my days a gay and joyous boast
   But fill them now with sorrow and confusion;
   And that my great delusion
   May more dishearten me, I represent
   The martyrdom I suffer day by day.
   Then, casting dreams away,
   I find myself so far from my intent
   That I remain a shadow in the shade:
Love has a wrong so real upon me laid.
When I perceive two simple creatures, wild
   And nimble things, who feeding stray afar
   Through grassy vacancies of green terrain,
   With tears I say to them, "O wise and mild
   Your lovers' life, for whom no hostile star
   Can make your hopes delusory and vain.
   One grove, one hill, one plain,
   One wish, one pleasure ever holds you both.
   But from my lady dear how wide am I!
   If tenderness can ply
   Your hearts, together hear my sorrow's growth."
   Then rousing, with a clearer mind I muse:
   To seek another is myself to lose.
Along the reaches of the lonely shore
   I follow Love, my old opponent fell
   Who most rejoices in my worst defeat.
   There, with the waves, my heart expends its store

In plaintive cries, and of a pointed shell
And level sand I make my pen and sheet.
Like bait that fishes eat,
Her lovely face allures me to my woe;
And ever in my mind her form discerning,
Both faltering and yearning,
I often pray that she may pity show.
Then I awake and with "O hollow thought,
Where is my lady?" weep and turn distraught.
O song, upon this beech you'll live beside
Your mate and with your mate will always be,
Just as my grief will always go with me.

"In this manner, ladies, love assails us from all sides; so everywhere, in all conditions, flames, sighs, tears, agonies, torments, and miseries pursue unhappy lovers, who, that the nadir of all sorrow may be reached in them, can never make peace, or even a truce, with these punishments of theirs since they are placed beyond all other human customs by their obstinate and savage fate.

"For all of nature's creatures which exert themselves in any way to keep alive are wont to rest after their toils and so to restore the powers which they feel that exercise has weakened. At night, in their sweet nests among the tranquil leaves, the cheerful birds recover from the spacious flights they made by day; throughout the woods the roving beasts lie down; the timid fish are couched on grassy river beds and light seaweed before they wheel again in widening circles; and most men likewise, who have performed their various labors all day long, when evening brings their limbs repose and sleep comes on, wherever it may be, take in security their sweet restorative from toil. But wretched lovers, whom fever ever kindles, have no rest or respite or relief from suffering; at every hour they are grieving; at every season they are torn by their divergent cares, as Metius was drawn apart by horses.

"Their days are sad, and the sun itself displeases them as seeming to be happy and so contrary to their own condition; but their nights are much worse because darkness, which better matches their misery, is more inviting to their tears than light. Their nocturnal vigils are long and lachrymose, their slumbers brief and painful and often no less filled with weeping than their vigils. As soon as their bodies fall asleep, their minds fly back to their old sorrows and, by deceiving the feelings with timorous fancies and newer forms of care, browbeat and terrify them. Their slumber is disturbed or, scarce begun, is broken; or if the wasted body clutches it as something necessary, the heart sighs as it wanders in its dreams, the spirits shudder with anxiety, the melancholy mind is grieved, and the eyes weep sorely, accustomed, when asleep no less than when awake, to serve the turbulent imagination. Thus lovers' nights are just as painful as their days and see them shed their tears as generously as they are sparing of their sighs by day.

"Nor do their tears lack water because their eyes have already flowed like fountains; nor are their sighs interrupted midway, nor do those of today come from the heart more smoothly or with less passion because all the air is packed with yesterday's. Nor do their griefs grow less by grieving, their laments by lamentation, their sufferings by being made to suffer; nay, every day impairs them more and hourly becomes more dire. Conceiving by himself, the miserable lover grows big with sorrow. He is that Tityos who fed the vultures on his liver; nay, he is forever renewing his heart to feed the thousand maws of unendurable vexations. He is that Ixion who turned upon his wheel of pain, now carried up, now down, yet never could escape his torture; nay, he is ever the tighter and more strongly bound the longer that he turns. For I cannot, ladies, do justice to the punishments with which this cruel master plagues us, except if, having reached the lowest pit of Hell, I lay before you the last tortures of the damned; and maybe even they, as you can see, are not so sharp as those of lovers.

"But now we must put a period to these arguments and cease to talk about these matters any longer, though the more one talks about them, the more one who has well considered them has yet to say. From what you have heard then, ladies, you should not find it hard to understand what Love is like, how harmful and how rude. We men, whom nature holds so dear, were through a special act of grace endowed by her with intellect, which is a divine power, in order that by means of it, leading a purer life, we might hasten our ascent to heaven; but he, in defiance of her majesty, maliciously despoils us of that power and with his foot holds us miserably planted in this earthy muck, where it is often our misfortune to be suffocated. Nor is it only the less famous or less worthy lovers whom he treats as you have heard, but even those who have attained a higher state; to show his scorn for seats of gold and jeweled crowns, he soils and casts them down with even less regard and decency than in the case of others. So if the first girl who sang to us accused him of causing her grief, you ought to thank her, Gismondo, except that she laid too unembittered and too brief a charge against that guilty cutthroat.

"But now I turn to you, Love, wherever in the ambient air you may be flitting for our harm; and if I accuse you with more rancor and at greater length than she did, it is no marvel, except that I upon whose neck you tread so heavily should still be able to bring forth these words; yet they, the utterance of a weakened, weary prisoner, are surely hoarse and scant in view of what your many crimes and countless homicides deserve. You nourish us on gall; you reward us with sorrow; you are the god most deadly and pernicious to our lives, and continually give us the bitter proofs of your fell deity; you make us prize our sufferings; you pretend to cheer us with sad things; you terrify us at all hours with a thousand new-fangled kinds of fear; you make us live in agony and guide us on the road to tragic death.

"And behold, what sport are you now having, Love, with me? Born a free spirit and greeted kindly by the world, in the bosom of my dear family I led a life which was secure and tranquil, passing my youth without a sigh or tear, happy if I had only never crossed your path. You gave me to her whom serving faithfully, I held more dear than life; and in that servitude, while she was pleased with me, for a good while I lived much luckier than one who has been made a prince. But what am I now, and what is now my life, O Love? Robbed of my dear lady, separated from aged and unhappy parents, who might have been content to die if they had not brought me into existence, naked of all comfort, distasteful to myself, long tossed from misery to misery at fortune's whim, finally become a byword to the people, dragging my heavy chains behind, for all my weakness I flee from company and ever seek some place where I may cast off this tortured flesh; but being tougher than I wish, it forces me to remain alive and endlessly to weep for my affliction. Alas, that it, at least for pity of my suffering, might rather melt away and by my death might feed her savage heart which wills me to feed mine on such a wretched life. But I'll not feed it long."

Here Perottino drew from his bosom a little handkerchief with which he wiped his overflowing eyes, as he had done already when he began to speak; then chancing to gaze at it, all tear-soaked as it had become, he wept still more freely, adding these few words to those he had already spoken, "Ah, my cruel lady's luckless gift, unhappy handkerchief, which serves for this unhappy work: in giving you she showed me clearly what my future state would be. You alone remain as my reward for countless sufferings; and since you are mine, let it not vex you if as long as I shall live (and that will not be long), I bathe you with my tears."

While he was speaking, he leaned forward with both hands pressed against his eyes, from which tears now fell in such abundance that none of the ladies or young men could check their own. At length, when he had remained for some time bent over in this way and motionless, the others, who had already risen to their feet, summoned him repeatedly and in the end, because they thought it time to go, raised him and sweetly comforted. That he might recover from those bitter thoughts, the ladies asked him for his handkerchief since they were curious to see it; and as it passed from hand to hand while they were walking to the portico, each of them was glad to examine it several times. For it was woven of the finest threads, fringed all around with gold and silk, and at the center bore a charming little animal which had been painted there in the fashion of the Greeks and whose careful workmanship revealed both a master's hand and a discerning eye.

After leaving the fair garden, the young men brought the ladies to the palace. Then, since Perottino did not wish to stay for the festivities, they descended once more; and discussing now one thing, now another, in order that he might forget his sharp anxieties, they spent the remainder of that day in wandering by shady banks and pleasant slopes.

GLI ASOLANI
BY MASTER PIETRO BEMBO
IN WHICH LOVE IS
THE SUBJECT OF DISCOURSE

Book Two

WHEN I think of it, I am struck by the curious fact that although nature has endowed us men with limbs subject to weakness and decay and a soul which is immortal, we generally devote ourselves, as far as we are able, to the pleasures of the body, while not many, or better, very few give so much thought to their minds. For no one is so abject that he will not clothe his person in some fashion, and many are those who lap themselves in diaphanous purple, dainty silk, nay priceless gold itself, and glitter with the rarest gems, that they may thus do greater honor to the body; yet all day long we see countless numbers who fail not only to adorn their minds with real and solid virtues, but even to shroud them in some vesture of good manners.

Furthermore, this earthly burden, which a few years will serve to nullify and turn to dust, fills us with such delight that although nature everywhere abounds with things fit to sustain it, we ransack the fields, the woods, the streams, the sea itself, in our desire for still more precious foods; and although a little shed affords all the protection that the body needs from sun and snow, to solace it we drag bright marble out of distant places and build wide palaces on every street. Yet we often take no interest in our celestial portion, neglecting to feed or clothe it, setting before it the bitter leaves of vice rather than the sweet fruit of righteousness, and holding it bound in the vile servitude of evil rather than inviting it to dwell with virtue's glorious achievements. When we feel some member of the body sicken, we take a thousand measures to restore its health, although we seldom care to minister to our sick souls: the result perhaps of our believing that since the body seems more important than the soul, it has more need of these attentions.

Yet this is not a wise conclusion; for not only does the body fail in reality to seem more important than the mind, but the mind obviously surpasses the other. It assumes as many forms as occupations, while the form of the body is ever one and the same; yet they can be known in a short time by everyone, while few men ever see the latter throughout its existence; and while this same body endures only a few days, the everlasting soul remains forever and for long ages can preserve what we accustom it to hold as it is lingering in the flesh.

If men gave as much consideration as they should to these and many other things which might be added to them, life on earth would be much more inviting and much sweeter than it is. Should we, without neglecting the body, adorn rather our minds, better nourishing them and giving them a more honorable reception, we would be worthier of them than we are and would take more care to keep them well; and were they sometimes to grow sick, we would strive more zealously to cure their maladies than we do now.

The words of Perottino in the preceding book have showed how grievous seems that malady, among others, with which love burdens us; yet Gismondo, who strongly disagreed with him, was far from that opinion. So, after dinner on the following day, when those fair ladies, as ordained, had come into the garden with the young men and, having reached the charming glade with its clear fountain, sat down within the laurels' shadow, after they and two of their companions had entertained themselves with various pleasantries at the expense of Perottino's views and all now waited for Gismondo to speak, he began as follows:

"Yesterday, my wise and comely ladies, Perottino brought his long complaint to a very pretty climax when he left us weeping, in order that he might win by tears what he saw himself unable to gain by words: namely, your belief in that of which he was attempting to convince you. What his tears wrought in you I shall not try to discover; but me, indeed, they moved to such pity for his misfortunes that I could not, as you saw, restrain my own tears. And this pity not only overcame me yesterday, but grieves me not a little every time I consider his many sufferings; his burdens, being those of a dear friend, always weigh upon me, almost as heavily, perhaps, as upon him.

"But take care, Perottino, that these very tears which may be praised in me as evidences of a brotherly and sympathetic mind may not perchance be blamed in you. For it beseems a man who ever since his childhood has been versed in profitable studies, as you have been, rather to trample his evil fortune boldly underfoot and make a jest of all its pranks, than basely to submit, weeping and complaining like some boy who has been roundly paddled. And even should he not have learned so wise a lesson from his old teachers or remembered from infancy how to meet and defend himself against a woman's blows (for fortune is a woman, if we may believe the gender of the word itself), he would do far better, and it would better suit a man enjoying his freedom, Perottino, to confess his weakness and accuse himself than to shirk his own responsibility by putting all the blame upon another.

"But what am I saying? He even designs it thus; and the better to conceal his own falsehood and weakness, he complains of Love, accusing him, condemning him, upbraiding him, laying every fault upon him, so that out of that free-handed patron of repose, that sweet messenger of joy, that saintliest preserver of mankind which Love has always been, he has in a moment tried to make a grasping thief of quiet, a bitter fount of agony, and the most wicked of all homicides. Into Love, as it were the common sewer, he has drained all the foulness of our lives, castigating him with such shrill and varied phrases that I am now inclined to think that Perottino is shrewder than we give him credit for being, since he has addressed us in this way, not so much to hide his faults as to reveal his eloquence; for I find it hard to believe that he should wish us, who know a peach from an apple, to assume that love, the only source of human happiness, is the cause of all our sorrow.

"O worthy ladies, he has surely poured so many falsehoods together and so well organized them with every appearance of the truth that he would undoubtedly, as he first threatened, flood me out, if I did not speak before such careful listeners as you, who are able to untie the knottiest questions and to judge them when untied, as you will shortly have an opportunity in this case. And in order to begin without delay, I shall consider the matter, provided you give me your attention. Nor should it be unpleasant for you ladies to do so since what I have to say today is more deserving of attention than what Perottino said yesterday. For not only is it more difficult to untie another's knots than tying them was in the first place; but by laying the truth before your eyes, I shall make you understand a thing which it is highly becoming that your tender age should know and without which all our existence might rather be called death than life, whereas he, when he lies to you, utters a thing which, even if it were true, would not be suitable to your years, but fitted rather to the dead than any to be found among the living."

Gismondo growing silent after this, Lisa, with a bold glance at Berenice, observed, "Madame, we shall have to listen to Gismondo attentively since his words ought to be very helpful to us; and if he fulfills his promise as happily as he made it, I am sure that today Perottino will need a defender as mighty as the assailant whose part he acted yesterday."

To these words Madame Berenice made some reply and then in glad expectancy awaited what would next be said; whereupon Gismondo resumed as follows: "Today I have one very simple thing to prove to you, my charming ladies, a thing which is known not only to me and to most of our young girls who have given rise to these discussions, but to everyone who lives, I believe, at least to some extent, perhaps to Perottino even, since he mentions it; and that is the excellence of love, against which he spoke such villainy as you heard yesterday, and spoke so wrongly, as you will hear today.

"But since I must cut through the dense undergrowth of his rank lies in order to reach the open ground of truth, I shall begin by answering his arguments. And to pass over the birth which he ascribed to Love, a subject of which I do not intend to speak, at the very outset of all he had to say, Perottino yesterday laid these two corner-stones and skillfully organized his whole case by erecting his arguments upon them: namely, that there could be no love without bitterness and that there is no bitterness which does not proceed of love alone. Now he argued the second of these ideas first, compelled to do so by your questions, Madame Berenice, for you soon perceived how gropingly he entered on his disquisitions, like one who wandered in the dark; so I choose to begin by answering that proposition with a few words, since not many are required to demonstrate its falsehood.

"I submit, therefore, that it is sheer madness to say there is no bitterness which does not proceed from love. For were this true, there would surely be no pleasure which did not proceed from hate, inasmuch as hate is no less the antithesis of love than pleasure is of bitterness. But because no pleasure can proceed from hate, which, insofar as it is hate, will always grieve the hearts which feel it, we must also of necessity conclude that no bitterness can ever in any wise proceed of love.—Do you see, Perottino, how I find weapons to defeat you? But let us come to closer grips with your arguments.

"When you cite the three kinds of evils to support your contention that every grief is derived from some love, as every stream flows from some spring, you argue on weak, fallacious grounds and support your case with weak, fallacious reasons. For if you mean that no grief would ever harry us were we not first in love, then love is indeed the fountain of all our afflictions, and it would follow that every grief is only love. But alas, why not tell us likewise that if men had not been born, they would never die; that being born is therefore the reason that we die; and, as a consequence, that the cause of Caesar's or of Nero's death is nothing but his birth? as if ships which have sunk at sea should complain to the monsters of the deep against the favorable winds which bore them from their ports, and not against those hostile gusts which overcame them, because, forsooth, if they had not set out from port, they never would have been engulfed. And granted that falling to the depths hurts only those who love the heights, we should not thence assume that the love we bear to wealth and honor, as you said, and not the fortune which removes them, makes us repine. For if loving them caused our minds a particle of grief, we should grieve both having and not having them; but the only time we grieve is when we lose them. Nay, it is obvious that the love of those things which fortune gives us only renders them sweet and pleasant; and if this were not true, the loss of them which fortune also brought to pass could hardly cause us pain.

"Then if we feel no sorrow in our love of fortune's gifts, except insofar as she, their mistress, alters them, and if love makes them only the more enjoyable to us, while she, according to her whim, bestows or filches them: why should you say that love rather than fortune causes the grief men undergo in their vicissitudes? Surely if while you banqueted at these marriage festivities with the rest of us, your servant, against your will, removed your plate which was heaped with the delicious things that he himself had set before you, and you complained about the cook, saying that it was he who caused your annoyance since he gave the food a dainty smack in order that you might be induced to eat it when it was served up: surely everyone would consider you mad. Now if fortune, in spite of us, removes the things which she has given us, since she is both our fairy godmother and our despoiler, and if you take love to task which gives them their attractive flavor, will you not seem to have gone mad? Little as I like to say it, Perottino, I am beginning to wonder if your unbridled melancholy may not have deprived you of your wonted sagacity in such matters.

"Although I shall not dilate my argument, one could reply in the same way to what you say about the gifts of mind and body, however they are administered. If your wild beasts grieve when they lose their suckling cubs, their misfortune, not the love which nature teaches them, makes them grieve. But concerning all these things what more can I now say which would not be excessive? except that while you have been shrouding your mendacity in these dark mists, you have drawn us no accurate

· 78 ·

picture of the truth, as if we perhaps desired no stronger argument than the one you used to prove love's bitterness, that by a clever turn the word *Venus* was originally formed from *venom* in order that the nature of the thing might be read upon its very brow. Not only was I ignorant of that etymology, but I believed that the actual qualities of things, not mere similarities of name, were to be weighed and studied. For if these similarities betray the actual qualities of things, I surely sympathize with you ladies, whom I have no doubt that Perottino will call the bugbears of men's lives inasmuch as the two words *dame* and *damage* are just as similar in sound as *Venus* is to *venom.*"

Gismondo's last words raised a winning smile in his fair listeners; and Madame Berenice was still smirking when she turned to the other two and said, "We are poor hands at the game, my friends, if we bring such disputations down upon ourselves."

To this Sabinetta, whose tender years and beauty added a sweet savor to her words, thus lightly answered: "Take it not amiss, madame; their debates do not concern us in the least. For tell me, Gismondo, which kind of dames would you have to cause the damage to your lives, the young ones or the old? Indeed, on your own premise, you cannot speak of the young ones unless they are of use to you, inasmuch as *youth* and *use* bear the same resemblance which you have found in *dame* and *damage*. If you will grant me this, we are contented to let you have the old ones."

"Let them be Perottino's," laughed Gismondo; "his

chilliness and tearful lamentations, since similarities are in order, are suitable to icy, querulous old age. But give me the youthful ones, whose gay hearts, packed with fervent hopes, will always chime with mine; and now more than ever I am sure they are of use to me, as you have said."

To these quips many others were added by the ladies and the young men, their happy repartee rebounding lightly back and forth; and with only Perottino silent, the chatter of that eager company, passing from jest to jest, might well have gone much farther had not Gismondo in this manner brought it to a close: "We have wandered far enough from the straight road of our discussion, my witty damsels, misled by Perottino's similarities; and since they are of no more use to us, however useful they have been to him, let us now leave them behind and take up his complaints again.

"You have already seen how false his proposition is that every bitterness derives from love; now let us see how much truth there is in that other postulate that love cannot exist without some bitterness. To prove it he has gathered so many kinds of bitter things that he would make an excellent farmer if he pulled up and cast out of his fields as many darnels, ferns, briars, burdocks, thistles, thorns, and other weeds as he has brought together sighs, tears, torments, tortures, agonies, and all the griefs and evils of our life, only to pile them on poor lovers' shoulders. And in order that he might begin this business with some apparent justification, he tells us that whenever writers speak of Love, they define him now as fire, now as frenzy, call lovers everlastingly unhappy, and complain about this god in every book, on every leaf; nor are their volumes merely full of tears and sighs, but stained throughout with lovers' wounds and bloody deaths.

"All this he rather uttered in resounding words, like something which he did not really feel, than proved by any rational demonstration. For who does not read on every page likewise of amorous pleasures? Who does not find in every book some lover telling, I shall not say of his good fortune, but even of his ecstasy? And if I now wished to mention as many examples as I could call to mind without much thought, I could linger the whole day on this subject alone and would fear that my voice might fail before my matter did. But because he used his songs to illustrate Love's savagery and the gravity of lovers' plaints (and he did well since he could not have found elsewhere such novel arguments as he thought to find in his own experience), if it will not displease you, ladies, I shall not refuse to say some songs of mine also, to show how much men vaunt themselves of love and with what reason."

All the ladies wished to tell Gismondo to proceed; but Lisa, who sat nearest him, silenced the others with her more prompt reply: "By all means do so, Gismondo, and not merely to please yourself, but because we beg it of you. Nay, I had already considered asking you if you had not offered it."

"There's no need for you to beg me," he answered on the spot; "for if it will please you to hear my rhymes, whatever their value may be, I shall be only too pleased to exhibit them to you. And furthermore, where Perottino seemed to take it amiss that you should deign to praise his poems, I should consider it a great honor and feel obliged for such a recompense."

"We shall gladly do so," replied Madame Berenice, "provided we can as honestly praise your work as we could his."

"Madame," said Gismondo, "you have imposed a hard condition; and I spoke unconditionally, rather as an eager suitor for your praise than as one who held a good opinion of his own powers. But come what may, I shall make proof of it"; and thereupon he pleasantly began:

Not the rarest summer air,
   Nor the drowsy ocean's long-resounding roar,
   Nor a lady debonair
   Passing like a pilgrim on some flowered shore,
   Are so fitted to restore
   A mind weighed down by its infirmity
   That I account them aught
   Beside the joy with which my heart is fraught
   Within, where Love is keeper of the key—
   Joy it is so sweet to me.

Although the ladies hung upon Gismondo's lips, expecting that more of his song would follow, he ceased and made a sign that it was finished. Then Madame Berenice resumed, "No doubt you have recited a charming bagatelle, Gismondo; but do you wish to be praised for so little?"

"No, my lady," he answered; "only I would like Perottino to tell me if he finds in it any of those sorrows of which he said that we could read in every song. But before he replies, hear this other, too:

O Love, my lord, faint and forworn this pen
  Of mine will never be,
  Or find satiety,
  In thanking you for honors all should ken.
  Of these my willing heart thinks gladly when
  It calls to memory
  Your generosity
  And from it gathers strength to thank again.
For you revealed me to myself complete;
  You first made me despise
  The ground and seek the skies;
  And to my speech you gave a music sweet;
  And she of whom my tongue will always treat
  You set before my eyes,
  And made my heart surmise
  A thousand thoughts both joyous and discreet.
To you I owe the happy life I lead,
  Who burn with gentle blaze,
  Whence fetching goodly rays,
  My heart on fair and honest hopes I feed;
  And if I ever reach that shore indeed
  Which my weak flight essays,
  Such joy will crown my days
  As does my wit no less than pen exceed.
He never felt true pleasure
  Who did not learn its measure, Love, from you.

This song enchanted the attentive ladies, and they said
various things in praise of it. But Gismondo, who found
time flying while he still had so much to say, broke in
with this continuation of his discourse: "If my rhymes

please you as you say, my amorous young women, it pleases me exceedingly. But you shall give me praises only when I shall have given all of his to Love; for it is not honorable for me to take so fair a recompense from you before my little work is yet completed.

"Now to come to Perottino: you see how falsely he argues that in amorous poetry nothing can be read but sorrow. Not only these rhymes of mine, who am a lover, but many others also may be read which praise and thank their master; and though there is no need for me to linger on these, since I must turn elsewhere, yet I shall mention one or another of them as they come to mind, so that you may better understand that crazy heresy of Perottino's.

"And surely if he had said that more lovers grieve at Love than eulogize him in their writings, his words would have been more reasonable, and I should have conceded him the point for the time being. Yet the fact that we see fewer praise Love than make complaint of him would not have been an argument sufficient to convince us that no love can be without its bitterness. For, granting that we are all by nature more inclined to grieve at our calamities than to eulogize good fortune, we may add that those who are successful in their love derive such pleasure from it that nourishing their minds and all their senses on that food alone, and in it finding their entire satisfaction, they have no need of either prose or verse or pages covered with absurdities. But the unhappy lovers, who have no other food to nourish them, no other outlet for their flames, run to the inkpots and there initiate such rumors as Perottino has so warmly painted for us.

"Hence we can see that lovers' lives are like the course

of rivers, which being more strictly dammed and choked with rocks or hedges, break through with all the greater force and tumble down with more uproar and foam, but which when they feel that their pathways are everywhere unhindered, spread forth their liquid beauties in repose and flow upon their way in perfect quietude. So lovers, the greater the impediments to their desires, the more they circle round them in their thoughts and, scattering the foam of their disdain behind, lament with all the louder grief; but if they are fortunate and everywhere enjoy this love without obstruction, they lead a spacious, tranquil life which no one ever hears about.

"If this is true (as it certainly is) and Perottino's bad arguments cannot make what is true untrue, is it not justifiable to say that unhappy lovers make all their complaints because they cannot still be happy? Who doubts that this is so? For were we to see ships painted in great numbers on the walls of a famous temple, some with broken masts and tangled sails, one wedged among a host of rocks or already vanquished by the waves it ploughed to its destruction, one lying disemboweled on the shore, and each giving evidence of its sad fortunes, yet we would not be therefore justified in saying that they may not have once made prosperous voyages, of which, as things irrelevant, no memory has been preserved. So Perottino can perceive, without my wishing to cite any writer, ancient or modern, how his frivolous arguments refute themselves.

"But not to hold you longer than necessary on this topic, now let us pass on to the miracles of love with their fine paradoxes: those who, like salamanders, live in fire, and those others who return to life when they are dying and similarly die of living. To these marvels God knows, not I, what answer should be made, save that I do not marvel at Perottino, who, either reassured by a foolish confidence that he can make us believe them or carried away by an unbridled appetite for grief, not only has allowed himself to pretend that such empty fables are the truth but has tried to confirm them with his own songs, as if those were the leaves of the Cumaean sibyl or words which Phoebus spoke from his prophetic tripods. Yet there is this redeeming feature, that judging by what I see in you and know in my own case, his songs have given us no little pleasure and once more mollified our spirits which were embittered by the harshness of his savage words. If they imparted as much truth to the mind as novelty and beauty to the ear, I would not clash with him.

"But what should I say now? Do not all of us know, without my saying it, that lovers no less than poets have a special license to feign things which are often far from any resemblance to the truth? to give their tongues or even pens new themes which none can rightly understand, subjects inconsistent with themselves which nature would never suffer to exist? Ah, Perottino, Perottino, how foolish of you to believe that you might make us think that lovers were allowed to do what nature cannot do, as if they were not men by birth and like the others subject to her laws. So I say your miracles are only lies; for they are no more true than what we hear of wandering Cadmus who sowed the dragon's teeth, or of aged Aeacus and his prolific ants, or of Phaëthon's rash journey, or of a thousand tales more strange than these. Nor are you the one who introduced this habit, but all the lovers who have written or who write have done and do the same, whether they have been happy or unfortunate in their affairs,—if indeed the happy ones are ever disposed to write or even speak of their felicity; and yet occasionally, if they were nurtured by the muses in delightful ease, they cannot long forget those first inamoratas even while they stir themselves in Venus's sweet sports.

"These generally tell the same fables that the sad ones do, not that they ever experience in themselves those miracles which the wretched often say that they experience; but these use them as various subjects for their writing, in order that by adding color to their inventions, they may make the picture of their love more beautiful in the beholder's eye. For what glad lover who composes does not fill his pages with the same fire which Perottino employs to reinforce the marvelous character of what befalls in love? and not only fire, but ice also and all those paradoxes which are more easily compiled on paper than in the heart? Who cannot say his tears are rain, his sighs are wind, and a thousand such witticisms which are as proper to a playful as a downcast lover? Who cannot in a moment convert his ladylove into an archeress who wounds men with the pointed arrows of her eyes? a thing which the ancients perhaps more slily feigned when they would often speak of huntresses and of their woodland prey, by lovely nymphs intending lovely women who with the barbs of penetrating glances slew the hearts of savage men. And these days who is not wont to compare his lady in a thousand other meta-phors more recent still?

"Spacious and wide-open, ladies, is that common field in which all writers walk, particularly those who being lovers, or writing about love, prepare to harvest the fruits of their genius and thus win praise. For in addition to feigning things which are impossible, not only do they gather the gay or sad material of their writings when they please, as it is most agreeable to them or to be had most easily, and on that base erect their falsehoods and most novel meditations; but they also twist a single subject to various purposes, and what one describes in joy, another shadows forth in grief, as if one kind of food, whether sweet or sour by nature, could be so flavored that it might have now one and now another taste according to the sauce that covered it. For however many lovers draw tears and lamentations and sharp torments from pretending to have lost their hearts, as you have often heard, it does not mean that I, in one of my effusions, am not to treat the same conceit as some playful marvel or delightful sport. And lest I argue in a void, listen to this miracle of mine:

At the first glance enchanted by your ray,
My heart, which none laid hold of hitherto,
Departing from me, turned to follow you;
And like a voyager who on his way
Finds some old pleasure long unused, my heart
Stayed gladly in those eyes which scattered light,
Still crying out, "Love lifts me to this height."

"Do you not see how lovers' hearts, as they imagine, can leave them because of their very joy and pleasure?

But this they still find no great wonder; more marvelous is that which follows:

But in your eyes the brazen vagabond
  Then mustered up such boldness bit by bit
  That, owing still to destiny, he quit
  That place and, passing inward, went beyond
Much farther than behooved his humble part,
  Till, coming to your very heart's redoubt,
  He rested there and roved no more without.

"Now you can see not only that our hearts leave us, but that they can even travel. Yet hear the rest:

But then your heart, swayed by some brave desire
  That it might never with another share
  Its realm (or maybe heaven led it where
  No other lord ought ever to aspire)
Went blithely where my own had made its start.
  Thus they exchanged abodes, and from that day
  Your heart with me and mine with you delay.

"Does not this miracle surpass all the others? that two loving hearts should each forsake its proper bosom to occupy the other's, and not merely without discomfort but by divine intervention? Yet why do I say 'this'? Whoever wished might cite so many fortunate examples that he could hardly bring them to an end.

"Now, Perottino, however little will suffice me in discussing this, you can see how much your fierce and cruel miracles avail you: if they are true because you and wretched lovers like you speak or write of them, true also must be these enchanting miracles of mine since I and happy lovers like me amuse ourselves in speaking or writing of them. For your miracles can no more prevent love from being sweet than mine from being bitter. If they are fables, let them return just as they left you, fables, and bear with them that well-painted image, nay even the imaginary portrait of your god, of which, had you not playfully spoken what you did, I would indeed have had something to say, and with reason. But you have corrected your own mistake, telling us not only that Love is not a god, but that he is only what we ourselves desire; and if I picked another quarrel in this matter, I should only, like that Penelope of long ago, reweave the cloth just woven."

Here Gismondo ceased; and before speaking again, while his memory deftly considered what next to say, he began to smile to himself. When the ladies, who still waited, saw this, they grew all the more eager to hear him; and Madame Berenice, having removed her weight from a young laurel tree which, growing on the edge of the clump and nearer to the murmurous fountain, as if bolder than the others, offered the double column of its two regular trunks to support her side, arose and said, "It is well, Gismondo, if you smile where I rather thought that you should be doubtful; for to my reckoning you have now reached that part of Perottino's discourse in which he deduces from human nature that there can be no love without continual suffering. If he will pardon me, I would gladly have you untie this knot, however tight it may be, and untie it as easily as that Penelope of long ago unwove the cloth just woven. But I'm afraid that you cannot, those arguments seem to have been wound and tied around so stout a weaver's beam."

"In a moment, madame, they will seem otherwise to you," replied Gismondo; "yet I do not greatly marvel at the view you have hitherto taken of them. Nay, just now when I was obliged to speak of them, as you correctly inferred, you saw me smile to think how Perottino could face his argument with so bald a lie that it had the air much rather of the truth than of the thing it was.

"If we examine his words, what he wishes we should believe to be true almost appears to be so, with the result that his dialectic turns white into red; for it seems very like the truth to say that every time a man does not enjoy what he loves, he suffers. But since he cannot wholly enjoy anything which is not wholly within him, it is not possible for us to love another without continual suffering. Now if this happens to be true, Timon of Athens was wise indeed, of whom we read that he shunned all men alike and neither loved nor sought the friendship of any man; and we also would be wise to expel this evil tormentor of our souls, renouncing all our friends, our ladies, our brothers, our fathers, our very children too, as if they were absolute strangers, and passing our whole existence without love, like some sea without a wave, except that we might wish to embrace ourselves as Narcissus did (for this kind of love I believe Perottino will not deny us since we must ever remain within ourselves).

"If you and everybody else, mastered by his arguments, do this, I am sure that he will in a short time not only dismiss love from the lives of men but likewise dismiss men from life; for if love ceases, the customs which tie men together also cease, with the necessary consequence that men and customs cease together. And if you tell me, Perottino, that I have no reason to fear such a cessation, since no argument of ours can make love fail among men and nature herself of very necessity disposes us to love a friend, a father, a brother, a wife, or a child, why must you then complain of love rather than of nature? If you believe she has been so bitter to you as you say, you should accuse her for not having made sweet the thing which she requires of us. But if you prefer to abide by your belief, you may undoubtedly examine it at leisure, for I think you will have no rival to dispute its ownership. Who is so poor of understanding as to hold that love of some valiant man or saintly woman, of the peace or laws or praiseworthy customs or good usages of some people, or of the people itself,—not to mention love of one, whether friend or relative, who loves you in return —brings, not grief or suffering, but even pleasure and delight? And all these things surely lie outside of us. Yet even were I to grant that they brought anguish to their lovers because they did not lie within us, would you have me likewise concede that the love of heaven, of the fair things that are above us, and of God Himself, none of which is contained in us since they are infinite and cannot be compressed in finite bodies such as ours, brings us to grief? You would never say this surely, for no misery can be derived from those celestial things.

"Therefore, Perottino, it is not true that the love we bear to extraneous things afflicts us because they are extraneous. But what would you say if, granting all these propositions out of friendship and accepting your very argument that no one can love another without grief, I should yet say that this love which we men make to the ladies and they to us is love, not of another, but of a part of one's self or, to put it better, of one's other half? For haven't you read that in the beginning men had two faces, four hands, four feet, and their other members similarly doubled? Then Jove, from whom men wished to steal his sovereignty, divided them through the middle and made them such as they are now. But because they would willingly have returned to their first perfection, in which they could do twice as much and had been twice as strong as they were since, each one, as he reached maturity, sought out his other half; and so all other men have done from time to time, and this is what we today call love or loving one another. Thus, whoever loves his lady seeks his other half, and the ladies do likewise when they love their lords.—Now what would be your answer, Perottino, if I spoke thus to you? Perhaps the same one which I made in regard to your miracles, that these are men's baubles, pictures and fables, mere inventions of their minds and nothing more.

"But these of which I speak are not mere pictures and inventions, Perottino. Nature herself, and not some man, declares all that I have told you. We are incomplete and lack part of ourselves if we are only male and female; for this which cannot exist by itself is not the whole, but only half and nothing more, as you ladies cannot do without us men nor we without you ladies. The truth of this is immediately evident if we consider that one sex by itself could hardly bring us into existence; and even were one sex sufficient for reproduction, when born we could not continue to live without the other.

"Our life, if well examined, is packed with endless labors which neither one nor other sex could wholly bear alone; nay, it would faint beneath its burden as camels out of distant countries sometimes do, which bear our merchandise across the weary sands eastward from Alexandria: if those who drive them chance to pile a double load on one poor camel's hump, the beast, unable to endure it, falls midway and remains. And, ladies, how could men plough and build and sail their ships if they must also perform those other duties which are yours? How could we at the same moment give the people laws and children suck, hearing complaints from one amid the others' wails? or lying in repose on featherbeds at home, wear out a heavy pregnancy, and at the same time make war beneath the open sky with sword in hand and clad in armor, defending ourselves and our possessions from assailants? But if we men cannot embrace both your duties and our own, much less ought we to expect the same of you, who are in general less vigorous than we.

"Nature foresaw this, ladies, from the first. And as it was easier for her to form us on one pattern like the trees, she divided us as if we were the two halves of a nut, placing our sex in one and yours in the other, and in this shape sent us forth into the world, where you were assigned tasks fitted to your weaker limbs and we were given those our stronger muscles were more apt to bear. Yet she joined and, as it were, mingled both under the yoke of stern necessity so that each, having need at times of the other, could not do without him or her, like two huntsmen of whom one carries the pannier and one the jug: although each bears a different burden on the road, yet when it comes to refreshing themselves, each does not consume his own apart; nay, seated in the shade, both share by turns what each of them has brought. So man and woman, though fated to bear different loads, each needs what the other carries to this hunt of life, being each too feeble to support more than his half of the common burden,—as anciently the women of Lemnos and the warlike Amazons learned to their sorrow when they attempted to become male as well as female, since by extending their jurisdiction to include both sexes, they brought both to their destruction. For neither men nor women can exist or maintain themselves without the other, nor does either sex by itself have more than half of what is needed to live or to be born since, as I said, what cannot exist by itself is only a part and not the whole. Therefore, ladies, I cannot see how we, or you for that matter, are more than parts; how you are not a half of us, as we of you; or finally, how male and female can be other than one whole.

"And when you consider it in such simple terms, are you not sure that your husbands always bear a part of you along with them? Eh, do you not always feel that a mysterious chain leads from your hearts to theirs, wherever they may go, and links you inseparably with them? Thus they are indeed a half of you and you of them, as I and my lady of each other. While I assuredly love her and shall forever love her, yet if we love interchangeably, each loves, not another, but himself; and other couples do and shall always do the same.

"Not to prolong this discussion, if lovers love with a mutual affection, they must undoubtedly enjoy the ones they love, even though, as you have argued, Perottino, no enjoyment can be derived wholly from another. And if they can enjoy what they love, while all our sorrow is due to nonenjoyment, I do not see how your conclusion follows, namely that love fills men's bosoms, as you said, with anxiety and perturbation.—Such, Madame Berenice, is the knot you doubted, not so long ago, that I could loosen; such Perottino's web, tied, as you said, around so stout a weaver's beam, a web indeed which seems rather to be one of Arachne's than like Penelope's firm cloth.

"But for all that, ladies, he neither repents nor in any wise refrains from the surpassing folly of his arguments; nay, as he dashes more and more wildly into this matter, like a nervous beast of burden, his words still lead him into longer and more senseless plunges, rejoicing in his own disaster. But sometimes, when a traveler who has reached a fork in the road selects the wrong way, believing that it is the right one, he will go further and further from his destination, the more he hastens to approach it; so when Perottino begins to discuss love as one of the afflictions of the spirit, striving, perhaps, to reach the truth, the more he exerts himself to speak of it and presses forward by the wrong pathway, the further from his mark he strays.

"Although anyone could demonstrate this to you in a few simple words, yet since it is not unseemly that I should reply to Perottino's alleged examples in a little more detail and also since dwelling on it in this way is suitable to the matter, I shall speak more methodically, if it is agreeable to you, and show you more clearly what his error is."

When the fair ladies had replied that they were pleased with what brought him pleasure and that if he was not weary of speaking as he did, they would never be weary of listening to him, he courteously thanked them. Then, having won their attention by extending his left arm towards them and begging them to give good heed since should they lose even a few words of what he had to say, he would have spoken to no avail, he closed his fist; and then, having raised two of the fingers like a fork, he began as follows:

"The ancient philosophers divide our soul, my ladies, in two parts. In one they place reason, under whose firm guidance the soul moves along a quick and certain path; to the other they assign those perturbations which mislead the soul into the most doubtful and abandoned byways. And because everyone desires to hold or takes pleasure in possessing what seems good to him, and similarly there is no one whom the anticipation of evil does not stimulate and there are few whom an evil which has already fallen does not weigh upon, the emotions of the soul are likewise four: desire, joy, anxiety, and grief, two of which arise from present or future good and two from evil which either has happened or may come to pass.

"But inasmuch as desire, when it can be effected reasonably, is healthy and, when it proceeds of a vicious appetite, is unhealthy, and joy is blamed in no one provided it does not go beyond the bounds of what is seemly, while the avoidance of possible evils is praiseworthy or shameful according to the good or evil nature of our fear, —the philosophers subdivide each of these three emotions into good and evil forms, assigning honest desire, honest joy, and honest fear to that part of the soul which is moved by reason, and to the other part the desire, joy, and fear which are excessive. The fourth, grief for present evils, they do not divide like the others; but because they say a wise and constant mind will never mourn over any of life's accidents and that sorrow for things which have befallen is always vain and excessive, they place this one emotion entirely among the perturbations. Thus there are three emotions which are wise and sober, four which are senseless and intemperate. Moreover, since it is certain that nature can do no evil and that only good can proceed from her, the philosophers affirm that the first three emotions, being reasonable and good, are likewise natural to men, while the other four, which they call disordered perturbations, occur contrary to the course of nature.

"Thus, ladies, as we saw, there are two roads before the soul: one that of reason, along which all the natural instincts move; the other that of the perturbations, by which the unnatural ones proceed to their destruction. Now you do not believe, I take it, that any unnatural instinct can abide with reason; for if it does, it must be natural, and how can that be natural which is not natural? Nor is it right to say that a natural emotion can be mingled with the perturbations, because in that case it would no longer be natural, and surely nothing could ever be both natural and unnatural. The passions of the soul having, therefore, been subdivided and considered as you have heard, you must constantly remember that no natural emotion can ever share our minds with any perturbation.

"Now, to return, Perottino placed love among the perturbations, reasoning thus: if it is something which enters us in spite of nature, the wretched thing cannot be placed elsewhere. But if it is an emotion given us by nature as something good, it cannot, while it accompanies nature, in any way be changed into one of the evil perturbations or proud and sinister emotions of the soul. What would, or should, I then say more, my shrewd young ladies? Must I show you that love is natural in us? This we did already when we spoke of the love which is felt for fathers, children, relatives, and friends. Even though I did not cite you, who are ladies, these very laurel trees which listen to us would still provide the evidence if they could speak."

Hardly had Gismondo ceased when Lavinello, who had been silent for some time, assailed him in these words: "If these laurels had spoken, Gismondo, they would ill support you in what you are trying to prove. If they resemble the original stock, as is the nature of plants, they have never loved; for that lady who first formed the trunk from which all these are sprung never experienced love, if what they write of her is true."

"You are mistaken, Lavinello," was Gismondo's immediate reply, "and you misjoin what nature kept apart. These laurels, as you say, resemble the original stock, but not the lady, who left her own nature behind as soon as she assumed their bark. Like their ancestor, they love the earth and are beloved of it; and after love has gotten them with child, they produce their pollen, fruit, and leaves, just as the laurel did from whom they all have come; nor do they cease to love before life ends,—a fidelity which would to God we human beings might imitate, that Perottino might not now perhaps have reason to weep so bitterly as he has done more often than I care to think. But since the woman, as you report, failed to return your love, a thing contrary to nature, she perhaps deserved to be turned into a tree, according to the legend. And indeed, what does it mean to change one's human limbs for those of wood, if not that one puts off sweet natural affections in favor of those which are unnatural and barbarous and harsh? If these laurels could speak and understand our words, I am inclined to think we would now hear that they had no desire to become men, since we are opposed to nature herself, a thing which never befalls them; not, however, that they are good evidence in this matter, Lavinello.

"Love, therefore,—and there is no need to search it further, ladies,—love is a natural affection of our minds and therefore necessarily sober, reasonable, and good. So, whenever an emotion of ours is not sober, not only does it fail to be reasonable and good, but by the same token it cannot be love. Do you hear what I say? Do you see where pure and simple truth has brought me? What is that emotion, you may well ask, if not love? has it any name? Yes indeed, it has many, and those happen to be the very ones Perottino gave it at the beginning of his discourse, when he was speaking about what he believed to be love: *fire, madness, misery, unhappiness,* and in fact, if I may call it by one phrase which is more appropriate than the rest, it is *every evil;* whereas love, as it will soon be clear to you, embraces every good.

"What more can I say? Do not, my ladies, be deceived by such simple words as *love* and *lover*, which others use so easily; do not hastily believe that all which men call love is really love or that all who are reputed lovers are lovers in reality. These terms are generally applied to every new desire, whether it is sober or otherwise; and once begun, the use of them is continued since it is supported by the idiotic persuasion of mankind, which makes no distinction in applying various names to its various acts and so includes among lovers both those who are ill-affected and those who are well-disposed toward the things which they desire and seek.

"Ah, how easily do men delude their wretched minds; how vain and foolish is their credulity! Perottino, you are not in love; it is not love, Perottino, which you feel; you are the shadow of a lover, not a real one, Perottino. For if you really loved, your love would be temperate; and in that case you would never grieve for what had happened nor desire what you could not have. Aside from the fact that grief in itself is always vain and excessive, it is stupid and woefully intemperate to go on seeking what cannot be had, as if one could obtain it. Poets, wishing to reveal this folly, invented the giants who sought to conquer heaven, making war upon the gods whom they had not the strength to overcome. If fortune has deprived you of the dear lady whose lover you would like to be, cease to desire her, since there is no other course open, and accept the loss of what you see that you have lost. Love her in simple purity, as many things are loved which we are hopeless of possessing. Love the charms at which you have already marveled, and praise them willingly.

If you cannot perceive them with your eyes, be satisfied to study them within your thoughts, a pleasure no one can deny you. And finally, love that strain in her which few men love today, thanks to the vice which has deprived us of all worthy customs: I mean the strain of honesty, which, as the special treasure of all ladies who are wise, ought ever to be dear to us, and all the more, the more we love them dearly. So I have long striven to make the honesty which appears in the person of my lady as captivating as her beauties are, although, when I first desired her, I found that quality a heavy burden to support, as reins and saddles are to inexperienced steeds. In confirmation whereof I then wrote the following song, which I offer you the more willingly, my gracious damsels, because it is more suitable to you, who are as honest as you're fair, than any of the other songs which have been yet recited:

Never such a thief of love or one so fleet
   Left her footprint on the grasses;
   Never nymph so comely lifted leafy bough
   Or spread along the wind such golden tresses;
   Never decked her gracious limbs in airy vesture
   Lady so resplendent and seductive as
   This lovely foe of mine.
One displeasure which we mortals seldom meet
   All my other plagues surpasses:
   Sweeter harmony than human ways allow
   Her beauty with her chastity professes.
   Thus the first possessed my heart at Love's mere gesture;

Yet my heart forgets to grieve, the other has
    A stroke so swift and fine.
Rose or lily never blooms in solitary peace,
    Far from all the world's ado,
    To which my soul, taught by the wish confined
    Within its walls, does not in turn compare
    That flower whose like no man has ever picked.
    So carefree loveliness in part relieves,
    In part revives my fire.
When a fondling ermine lays his guileless fleece
    Before me, I renew
    My sense of that strange whiteness of her mind
    From thought of which I never may forbear.
    This very witch of late so well has tricked
    Me of myself that unlike other thieves
    She purifies desire.
Rivulets, when winter ice to water turns,
    Never run with such a spate
    As from her smooth and stately forehead wells
    That sweetness which can make our hearts content
    Yet never from their righteous course depart;
    Nor does the tranquil ocean lie at rest
    So quietly as she.
If the wind assails a torch that dimly burns,
    Its flame will suffocate;
    So my wishing only that in her which spells
    Her virtue has less worthy pleasures spent.
    Lucky is the veil in which my prescient heart
    And she are wound, who otherwise were dressed
    With less propriety.
All the pleasure it imparts to be alive

Is owing to her sway
Who alone withholds me from the common jar.
She has taught my soul so well to follow where
I hear her that it will no elsewhere go,
But by that road more ceaselessly endeavor
The more Love urges me.
Sweet the destiny which thus has made me strive;
Sweet to have my heart a prey,
Close within another, from myself so far;
Harshness sweet and sweet my long-enduring care;
Sweet the miracle which men so seldom know;
Sweet each anguish which your merit makes forever
Most enchanting company.
Far and wide as Love may search, such beauty never
Was so honest, nor will be.

"Now, ladies, to return to the point from which we
strayed, you can see what kind of an error Perottino
makes and where he has found it: while he ought to
take that pathway of the mind which would lead him,
as he spoke of it, to love, he has reached its opposite
through setting out upon the other road, by which he
has encountered all those woes, those agonies, those care-
worn days, those nights so full of sorrow, those scorns
and jealousies, those murderers of other men and sometimes of themselves, Metius and Ixion and Tityos and
Tantalus; and in the end he sees himself among them, as
if reflected in clear water, yet does not recognize his
plight too well since otherwise he would have grieved
and shed much truer tears than he has done. For through
believing that he was in love while he met his lady only

in imagination, he has become a solitary stag whom, like Actaeon, his hounded thoughts have pitifully torn; but he seeks to nourish rather than escape them, desiring to bring his life to an untimely end and not aware, apparently, how much better it is to be alive, on any terms, than dead. It is almost as if he were tired of the world and hoped to gather no more fruit from his succeeding years, though they have hardly yet begun to flower. But, ladies, for all his weeping drains away and spoils this fellow's youth, as you can see, he is no older than I am; and the number of my years is still two less than there are days within the shortest month. Yet he, as if he were nearly a hundred, like one hopelessly sick, is ever asking who will bear him away into another land, telling himself that a change of air will perhaps restore his health.

"O wretched Perottino, and indeed wretched, since you yourself go in pursuit of your misfortune and, not contented with your own, endeavor to make all men your companions in this misery. For all men, of necessity, are lovers; and if lovers were always attended by those excessive appetites, those joys so dreary, those sorry forms of dread, and those agonies which you describe, you would not only, doubtless, make men miserable but constrain each one of them to become misery itself. (I pass over those savage miracles which you told us that your god performed, miracles sufficient not only to render human life both harsh and bad, but even to cloy Hell and all its depths.) How much better it would be, you dolt, to end your unprofitable melancholy than every day to undergo still sharper grief! how much better to look to your salvation while it is still possible, than to cling obstinately to your perdition! how much better to realize that nature did not bring you into the world in order that you might abandon it, than thus, by doting on imagined griefs and butting with the wind, to withdraw from your true feelings and your security itself!

"But to lay aside Perottino with all his fabrications, whose long complaining yesterday of love has occupied more of my reply today than I would wish: we are not so foolish, ladies, as to think that grief is caused by love alone, which indeed has no share in it, or that love is not possible without bitterness, whose flavor never spoils a lover's sauce. And since the weapons Perottino grasped with a mind so ill-disposed to Love have had their edges blunted on another's shield, as if they were of lead, let us consider those with which Love arms his champions, though yesterday Perottino believed that none would be left for me to grasp. Yet to my way of thinking I could hardly handle all of them unless I felt myself much more redoubtable than I am; and even though I could, the whole day would not be long enough, much less this slender midday which has been assigned,—were it not, my dear young ladies, that you wished me to add something to what we have already discussed."

"We would not limit you in any way," replied Madame Berenice when she had found how her companions thought; "nor do we feel that you should stop. In fact, we are impatient to have you finish the discussion you began by promising to us. But there's no need to hurry; for though you may think you have spoken long enough, look at the sun and you will see there is plenty of time before it will grow cool. Nor is it any wonder since we came here earlier today than yesterday. Furthermore, we might very well have lingered here somewhat longer than we did, for the entertainment began a good deal later than we believed it would when we arose with you. So, Gismondo, you may have the satisfaction of continuing to discuss at length the thing of which you most enjoy to speak."

The lady's words were pleasing to the young man, who had at first been half afraid that his discussion might be much curtailed by lack of time; but since the shadows of the laurels revealed that it was as she had said and he had reason to hope that they could stay here longer than the day before, he cheerfully made ready to continue.

And behold, two doves which were whiter than snow came winging down the slope and, after hovering above the heads of that gay company, descended fearlessly to rest beside each other on the graceful fountain's brim. There they remained for some time, murmuring and kissing lovingly, to the great pleasure of the ladies and the gallants, all of whom looked on in silent wonder. Then, dipping their beaks into the water, they began to drink and soon to bathe themselves with such domestic ease before everyone that to the ladies it appeared the sweetest and the most delightful thing in the world. But while they were sporting thus, secure from all anxiety, a rapacious eagle, dropping like lead from I know not where, almost before he had been seen grasped one of them between his talons and bore her off. The other screeched with dread and would have drowned herself in the fountain; but she finally emerged with difficulty, weak, tremulous, and heavy from her wetting, and beating her wings to dry them as best she might, flew slowly off before the eyes of the company.

The dove's swift capture shocked the tender-hearted ladies and made them all expostulate, nor could they cease to marvel how that innocent bird had been so shamelessly abducted from their very midst. Each cursed the hateful eagle many times, not without the young men's lamentations too; and all of them spoke together, one about the first dove's misfortune, one about the fear the second felt, and one about the tameness and the beauty of them both; and some of them, looking more deeply into the matter, wished to believe that what they had seen had not occurred by chance. Finally, when Gismondo saw that the ladies were done, he began:

"If our dove was carried away by her abductor just as lovely Ganymede once was, her companion may find it less disheartening to have lost her, and we may wrongly blame the proud eagle whom we have taken so to task. But inasmuch as to grieve further about these things which we cannot amend is surely a waste of energy, let us forget our grief along with Perottino's and enter now upon love's beneficence, according to the promises I made you."

Then, before he could continue, Lisa, full as she was of an endearing playfulness, more to test him than for any other reason, said, "This is a strange time, Gismondo, for you to lay your original reflections aside, particularly now that this event has left us all in doubt. For if we feel grief because we have seen that poor little creature in the talons of her enemy, and love because we have been attracted by her comeliness, it clearly follows that we can love and grieve at the same time; and here you might have to face the criticism uttered daily, that words are very far, in general, from the fact."

At this point Gismondo smiled toward the ladies and replied, "You have heard her argument. But, Lisa, you are not going to snatch the truth out of my grasp as easily as the eagle snatched away our silly dove just now; for I shall defend the truth. You are continually leading me back to the position we left behind some time ago, when I demonstrated that the loss of the things we love is caused, not by the love which makes us desire them but by the ill fortune which plunders us of them. We can, as you say, both love and grieve, but not grieve because of love. Furthermore, the love which mingles with the passions is not really love, although it is called and considered such by the majority of people. But I am not inclined to discuss this or similar matters again at greater length than I have already done, although I have done so in many other cases. They should suffice you, provided you are not determined to be obstinate, a fault as common in fair ladies as restiveness is in well-favored horses."

"If restiveness were found only in well-favored horses, Gismondo," replied Lisa, her whole face blushing, "I who am not fair" (yet she was as fair as any flower) "might consider myself able to speak wisely without giving you reason to consider me obstinate. But since that vice is more apt to occur among the ill-favored than the others, you have certainly found means to silence me today, albeit I shall repay you afterwards."

After that gay company, what with these words and

others, had rallied Lisa on her blush, Gismondo cut short all the remarks which might force him to deviate from his argument and came to it directly in this fashion: "The kindliness of love, of which I am about to speak, O ladies, is surely infinite; and though it be called in question, its full extent can never be revealed to those who only hear of it. Nevertheless, whatever can be revealed through discussion will be most easily understood if we consider how much love succors and delights us; for the larger any fountain is, the larger are the streams that flow from it.

"To begin then with its benefits: it is obvious that everything is more salutary as it produces more and greater benefits. But since love is the cause and source, not only of numerous great benefits but of all there are beneath the sun, it is surely more salutary than all the other salutary things the world contains. Oh I know that you prudent ladies will begin to think that I make too much of love, as if I would graft the head of Atlas on the shoulders of some middling fellow; but indeed I say only what is fitting and nothing more. So look around you, my fair young women, and consider how fruitful is the world, how many and how various are the kinds of living things in it; yet there is none among them all which has not been derived from love as from its first and most reverend father. For unless love joined two separate bodies formed to generate their like, nothing would ever be conceived or born; and though living creatures fit for generation were brought together by main force, unless love took a hand and moved their minds with one desire, they might bear company a thousand years and never breed.

"In their season the male fish are sought among the moving waters by their eager wives and gladly yield themselves so that a mutual desire propagates their kind; the ardent birds seek one another in the spacious air; the beasts likewise, when they would have their mates, seek them among the darkest woodland haunts. And all of these, according to one law, through loving make their brief lives eternal. Nor is it only sentient creatures which owe their existence to love, but all the forests too would have no rooted form or quality without the same; for, as I said about these laurels, if the trees were not to love the earth and the earth them, they could never find the means to raise their trunks and clothe themselves with foliage. These flowers and these very blades of grass beneath us would not have been brought forth to make this soil so green and charming or spread for us so fair a carpet, if natural love had not mingled their seed and roots with the ground in such a way that when it freely gave that tempered moisture which they sought, each lovingly embraced the other and they were joined in procreation.

"But why speak of these flowers and this grass? Surely, if our parents had not loved one another, we would not now be here or anywhere else; and I would not have come into the world, as I have done, if for no better reason than at this moment to defend our guiltless love from Perottino's savage calumnies. Nor, ladies, does love merely bring human beings to the point of birth, which is their first existence, but it gives a second life as well,—or I should rather call it their principal life—that is, the life of virtue, without which it would perhaps be better not to have been born or better to have died at birth. For men, as Perottino said they did at first, would still be wandering up and down the mountains and the woods, as naked, wild, and hairy as the beasts, without roofs or human converse or domestic customs, had love not persuaded them to meet together in a common life. Then, abandoning their cries and bending their glad tongues to speech, they came to utter their first words; and scarcely could they talk to one another when, condemning the tree trunks and jagged caves which had been their homes, they began to build their crofts and, leaving their wild nuts, to hunt the savage beasts with which they once had lived.

"Little by little, as men lived in this new way, love gathered strength, and with love grew the arts. For the first time fathers knew their own children from those of other men, and grown-up children hailed their fathers, and the delightful yoke of holy marriage bound man and wife together in shamefast honesty. Then villages were newly filled with houses, and cities girt themselves with walls for their defense, and laws were made to guard praiseworthy customs. Then friendship, which clearly is a form of love, began to sow its hallowed name through lands already civilized, and thence to sprout and grow and bear such tender blossoms and delicious fruit that the world still holds it dear, even though a gradual degeneration down to this pernicious age of ours has spoiled it of its first sweet odor and pure taste. In those days there were women glad to mount their husbands' funeral pyres;

there was Alcestis, never to be praised enough; there were such faithful, loving pairs of friends as Pylades and Orestes, who held their magnanimous dispute in pitiless Diana's sight. In those days Holy Writ began, and to their ladies eager lovers sang the earliest poetry.

"But why do I go on discussing love's mighty forces in such tame and feeble terms? This very fabric of the world which is so large and fair, and which it needs our minds rather than our eyes to understand, comprises everything; yet if it were not full of love, which binds it all together with the chain of its own discordant elements, it would never have lasted long nor would it be here now. So, ladies, as you see, love is the cause of everything; and necessarily, in that case, it must also be the cause of every good thing everywhere. For the more and greater benefits a thing bestows, as I have said, the more salutary it is; and hence you may conclude that love is the most salutary of all salutary things.

"Now tell me, Perottino, do you still think there is no weapon left for me to grasp? or none which I have not yet seized upon?"

Here, before anything else might be said, Madame Berenice interposed and, as if she would aid her, like a sister, in some way, with her own left hand grasped Lisa's right, who sat beside her, and turning boldly to Gismondo, said, "Since you could bite so well that Lisa now wishes to have nothing more to do with you, it seems possible that you did it in order that we might not bother you so much; and I would like to take her for my ally, although she may be an Amazon of little prowess from now on. But I ask you: if love, as you say, is the

cause of everything and it therefore follows that it is the
cause of every good thing everywhere, why do you not
add that it is equally the cause of every evil thing everywhere? for this will necessarily follow too, if your argument is to be accepted. If my prayers must be ascribed to
love because I owe my birth to it, the evil which I speak
must also be ascribed to it because, had I not been born,
I would not have said it. And so I can draw you the same
conclusion about all other things and people. Now if love
is no less the source of every evil than the foundation
of every good, I don't see why it is not just as harmful as
it is salutary."

"Oh yes, you see, madame, I think you see," Gismondo
hastened to reply; "for I don't believe you have so short
a memory that you have already forgotten what I said to
you just now. But in a matter where your companion has
received no offence from me, you would like to vindi-
cate her by involving me, as she did, in those disputes
we have already left behind. Do you not remember that
I said every natural thing was good and that love, which
is a natural thing, is always good likewise and never can
in any way be evil? For it is indeed the cause of the good
you do since it brought you into the world solely to do
good; but if you do anything evil, as I cannot believe that
you do, you should lay the fault to some disordered and
unnatural appetite of yours, and not to love. This life is
given us in order that we may act virtuously and not that
we may use it badly, just as some craftsman shapes a knife
to serve for men's good uses, but if you or I employ it
to do murder, the guilt is ours who have committed the
misdeed, and not the craftsman's, since he had no evil

purpose in mind when he forged the instrument by which the evil deed was done.

"But if you ladies are agreeable, let us turn to love's amenity: a thing, however, which it is most difficult to set forth in words since one can much sooner feel than tell its quality and power. As a painter can delineate the whiteness, but not the coldness of the snow, for something which can be appreciated only by the touch is not revealed to the eye, whose proper field is painting: so I have to some extent been able to describe love's benefits to you, but love's delight, which captures all the senses and overflows them all as if it were a fountain much more plentiful than this beside us, can never be conceived by ear alone, however long we speak of it. One thing, however, comforts me, that you yourselves have learned from experience, and still are learning, what that pleasure is, so that however little I may say of it, you will remember much, as much perhaps as if one could describe it wholly.

"But where shall I begin, my most delightful lord? How shall I broach your joys which are incomparable, ineffable, and infinite? Teach me since you have formed them, and guide me as I ought to go. And now then, in order not to mingle parts which please us separately, let us first discuss the pleasures of the eye alone, since these are commonly the first in love."

After a brief silence, which made his audience more attentive, Gismondo began: "Ladies, a lover's sight is not like that of other men, nor do enamored youths perceive the objects of their gaze with so little benefit as those who are not lovers do. For merely by moving his wings Love scatters such sweetness in his clients' eyes that in a moment it purges them of all blindness and makes those which were once dim-sighted grow marvelously keen, so that they find their greatest joy in seeing what is sweet to see; whereas other men take little or, frequently, no pleasure in the sight of daintiest things. And although many objects which we examine every day are sweet, sweeter than all the rest that any eye beholds are comely ladies such as you. Not that they reserve their charms for lovers' eyes, as if Love gave only those the power to search his treasuries; but though there is no man whom your grace and beauty do not in some way please, his pleasure falls as much behind a lover's as one flower is surpassed by all the pageantry of spring. Thus it frequently happens that when some handsome woman has been espied by many men, the sight of her is welcome to them all; but for the one or two who gaze on her with keener pleasure, there are a hundred who hardly give a second glance. Yet should her lover be among them and catch sight of her (a matter in which he is not apt to be the last), it is as if a thousand rose gardens were flowering around him, and all at once he feels each chamber of his heart dilated with such joy that it expells whatever sorrows his misfortunes may have packed together there.

"He studies and restudies her intently with fixed glance, and running over all her features with that delight which only lovers know, he lingers now on her comely hair, more like gold than anything else, hair which, like yours—and do not take it amiss that in discussing fair ladies I should use your various charms by way of illustration—hair which, I say, is parted straight down the middle of her lovely scalp and wound in many curls behind, but falling on either side of the temples in two flowing locks that sweetly fan her cheeks with every breath of air, would seem to be clear amber, blown, by some miracle, across fresh drifts of snow. Now he perceives the calmness of her forehead, whose glad expanse reveals unerring honesty, and under the darkness of her humble brows the large black eyes which mingle gravity with native charm and shine like two lovely stars on their ecstatic course, so that he calls a thousand blessings on his luck as well as on the day he first beheld them. Then he gazes on her tender cheeks, whose fine candor he compares to milk, save that in their more vivid coloring they sometimes vie with morning roses. Nor does he cease to scan the little mouth below, the sweetness of whose ruddy lips might tempt the coldest and least amorous to kiss. And furthermore, while he commends that portion of her snowy bosom which he sees, the unseen part wins even warmer praise; for his sharp eye discerns and measures it, thanks to the courteous dress whose subtle cloth, in spite of custom, does not always hide the beauty of those breasts, but often yielding to their shape, reveals it."

Those last words made the happy company turn their attention to Sabinetta's bosom, which it seemed Gismondo meant to describe rather than some other, since that lovely girl, who for her youth as well as for the heat was clothed in the lightest of materials, revealed two round, firm, unripe little breasts beneath her clinging robe. As a result of being stared upon she grew abashed and would have done more than that had not Madame Berenice, perceiving it, said suddenly, "This lover of yours, Gismondo, is certainly a bold, observant peeper who searches the very bosoms which we hide. I'd rather not have him inspect me quite so close."

"Madame, you conceal the advantage you derive from it," replied Gismondo. "For if I were to speak further, I would say that lovers go everywhere by means of their eyes and that from what openly appears they easily behold what is hidden; so, though you hide yourselves from other men as much as you will and can, my fair ladies, you neither can nor ought to hide yourselves from lovers. And yet Perottino will say that lovers are blind; but he is blind himself, since he does not see what there is to see and deludes himself, not when he sees—for what does not exist, nay, what cannot exist, cannot be seen—but when he describes a naked boy with wings and fire and arrows, like some new-fledged chimera, and feigns, as it were, to gaze in one of those glasses where men are accustomed to see marvels.

"But to return to the lover of whom we were speaking: while he studies both what I have and what I have not told, searching all with his keen vision, he feels so great a pleasure steal along his veins that he is not aware of ever having felt the like and asks himself, 'What is this sweetness warming me? What other moment ever brought me greater joy? O marvelous discernment wrought by love!'—things never said by those who do not love the woman they behold; for without love both sight and soul are drowsy in the body, both eye and brain are sleeping in the head.

"But this is not the last of all the joys which reach his heart by passing through the eyes. There are others that may come to him at any moment, such as seeing his lady with her companions tread the happy meadow grass; or stroll along green banks by limpid streams; or in soft breezes walk the willing seashore's sandy spine, on which she writes warm verses to her watching lover; or in some smiling garden pluck dewy roses from their stems, a gift perhaps intended for the one who sees her; or as she dances, move her artless, well-knit person in time to the resounding instruments, now winning admiration with her stately steps, now charming everyone with her enchanting turns and lithe delays, now with her quicker motions striking the beholder's eye like some onrushing sun. And all these things may be enjoyed by novices not yet established in their loves; but were we to speak of their enjoyment at its height, I am convinced that not all the pleasures felt throughout their lives by all the men who do not love would ever touch that one delight a single lover feels during the brief moment that lingering with his lady, he boldly studies and restudies her and, while their warm, unsteady glances suck draft on draft of sweetness, each makes the other drunk.

"Alas, why do I waste time and words on things which, whether they please much or little, are pleasing in themselves and somehow always gratify whoever sees them? for I have still to deal with those whose sight, although it sometimes brings immeasurable joy to lovers, is wont to trouble other men. How difficult it is, my dear young ladies, to scrutinize, if only with the mind, and much more to explain, the sacred force of love! What can be more bitter than for one to see those who are dearest weep? and who so brutal that he can watch their falling tears unmoved? Yet sometimes when a lover sees that the lady whom he holds dearer than all the world is weeping, just as I have said, he feels a kind of joy and exultation far greater than all other men are wont to take in all their laughter."

Hardly had Gismondo said this when Madame Berenice broke in, "Indeed I would not like my husband to derive a kind of joy and exultation from my tears. Nay, to speak the truth, Gismondo, if I found him doing so, I would hate him for it; and maybe, if I could, I would give him reason to weep also, while I in my turn laughed at him."

The other two young women followed suit, reaffirming what she had said and adding that it would be only courteous of Gismondo if he wept frequently before his lady in order to give her that pleasure; and all of them joined in the sport, seizing with great zest on this new occasion to make fun of him. But when he had let them laugh and chatter for a while and often conquer him, fixing his eye on Madame Berenice, he said, "You must be very cruel and lacking in compassion, madame, if you wished to make your husband weep. But unless I am mistaken, your face does not reveal so much ferocity. Nay, you show yourself the sweetest and most pleasant creature who ever lived; and I am sure that if Boccaccio's young hermit had seen you when he first left his cell, he would not have asked his father for any other goosey to take away with him and feed."

Here Madame Berenice fell silent, gazing, betwixt astonishment and shame, at her companions' faces. Lisa, who had been waiting for Gismondo to catch another in his net and give her a comrade in her misery, laughed to see her friend thus halted and, drawing close to her, said, "Madame, I am very glad that the same hail which blasted my harvest has now stricken yours. Since even you have not been spared, I need no longer grieve at what Gismondo did to me. I tell you, madame, his tongue will suffer no restraint today; and therefore I beg you, do not try him further, for he attacks like a flail, from all sides at once."

"I have already found him as you say, Lisa," Madame Berenice replied. "But take your own course, Gismondo, since you can for the moment silence us at will. For my part, I am resolved not to open my lips from now on."

Gismondo, to whom the ladies thus allowed a freer hand, proceeded: "The lovers' joys already told will serve to make you understand the ones not told, which are undoubtedly so great, at times so novel, and frequently so keen that it need henceforth cause no wonder if Leander often swam across a wide and dangerous strait in order that he might gaze on his lady for a little. Now we must turn to that other sense which carries voices to the heart, a sense which it is fair to say brings us no less delight; for hearing can provide the lover with as many forms of joy as seeing does, and as one object will gratify our eyes in various ways, one voice will also give our ears a thousand kinds of happiness.

"But what more is there for me to tell you of this pleasure which is not just as clear to you as me? Do you not know how great a satisfaction young women feel when they can speak freely with their lovers in some solitary place, perhaps within the gracious shadow of young trees as we are doing now? There none but Love attends, who at such times is wont to be no less the comforter of fears than the discreet ear-witness of their talk. Do you not already know how great a tenderness consumes two loving souls when they by turns describe what has befallen them? how they inquire and reply and beg and give their thanks? Do you not know how joyfully each listens to every word and sigh and murmur, every tone and accent of the other?

"Whose stony bosom is so cold to every amorous spark that he is not aware how dearly lovers like sometimes to recite their poems to their ladies, sometimes to hear their ladies do the same? or to parallel their loves with those of which they read in ancient times and to find their own reflections written in another's book, so that they meet within its pages what they have felt at heart and from comparing both derive the sweetest wonder? or with what pleasure our souls are wont to harken when our ladies sing their charming songs, especially if their light hands accompany the sound on some harmonious instrument? and with what further pleasure if they should sing some song of ours, or one perhaps of theirs? Letters and poetry, it is true, are almost proper to us men; yet just as Love, when he resides within our minds, will frequently instruct us in these arts according to the lesson of your eyes, so also when he enters your young bosoms, he will on occasion draw from them some rhyme or verse which we hold all the dearer as it is more rare in you. Thus, while our ladies more than double the sweetness of their harmony, they also reinforce our pleasure, which so delights the soul it enters that nothing can exceed it; for since the soul ever desires those celestial harmonies it left behind when it descended into the body, the taste of them makes it fall more joyfully in love with these than it seems possible that one should love an earthly thing. Nay, harmony, my ladies, is not a thing of earth, but even like the soul; for there were some men long ago who said the soul was nothing but a kind of harmony.

"But to return to our inamoratas, who multiply the sweet accord of voice with instrument in all the ways that I have said: what soul who hears them is so gloomy, so sick at heart, so weighted with his stormy thoughts that he does not grow glad and calm again? Among such happy and melodious sounds who is unable to forget his crosses and adversities? The poets tell how Orpheus, when he passed down through Hades with his lyre, silenced the barking with which Cerberus was wont to greet all comers; the Furies laid their anger by; the vultures of Tityos, the rock of Sisyphus, the fruit and drink of Tantalus, Ixion's wheel, and all the other torments ceased to rack their culprits, for all of them straightway forgot their offices, delighted by that song. And this myth is only another way of saying that heavy cares, which necessarily afflict the minds of men the great part of all their lives, cease to torture them when they forget their miseries, being ravished by their ladies' voices as by that of Orpheus.

"They who have experienced this oblivion know its power to remedy and alleviate our sorrows, necessary as it is that men should sometimes discover a solace for their woes and put some pleasure, like a wall, between the mind and their black thoughts. For just as the body cannot endure its toils without occasional repose, the mind cannot remain steadfast in grief unless some pleasure intervene. Such, Perottino, is the sad oblivion in which, as you observed, the memory of lovers is engulfed; such are the poisoned medicine, the wormwood, and the drunkenness which you ascribed to lovers.

"Yet should these pleasures, like those which I have said the eyes receive, reach, as they often must, the ears of men who do not love the ladies who produce them, you may be sure they do not really penetrate their hearts. For if the gardener of this place were not to walk along the trough of our canal removing stones or branches or whatever else might fall in it at any time, it would soon become so clogged that water from the fountain could no longer flow out through it; and in the same way, even striking harmonies will fail to pierce the ear which love has not unsealed. Who does not know that if my lady's voice were somehow to reach us in this spot, none of you would catch that sweetness in it which I hear? And if you likewise heard your husbands' voices, none of you would take such satisfaction in those belonging to the others as in her own dear lord's.

"But to proceed: because I have showed you ladies the pleasures which arise from these two senses, do not assume that I would also like to show you those which are owing to the other three; that would take me further than I now intend to go. Let Love guide you, who knows all the ways by which to reach those pleasures which our humanity desires most. What sweeter or more welcome leader could you have than he? None, surely; for he makes those pleasures as dear and sweet to us as he himself, and without him they have as little worth or taste as water does. So take him boldly for your leader, my pretty girls; and as a reward for the toil I spend today in his behalf, I pray that he may ever guide you happily. But come with me along this other road.

"In addition, then, to the five senses, which in men are the instruments of the mind as well as of the body, there is also thought, which since it belongs wholly to the mind, is far more excellent than they. Furthermore, the animals do not share it with us as they share our other faculties; for they see and hear and smell and taste and touch and possess all the internal senses which we have, but they do not deliberate or use rational discourse or have, in brief, the faculty of thought which we enjoy. This, however, is not of greater value solely because it is proper to men, who have their other faculties in common with the beasts, but rather because the senses can perceive only those things which are present both in time and place, while thought can leave the present, returning to the past at will or even leaping into the future, and can at one moment comprehend things both near and far; under this single name it sees and hears and smells and tastes and touches and in a thousand other manners shapes and then reshapes, for it could not be satisfied with all the senses of one man, nor yet with those of all men living. Thus, if we consider it well, we can see that it bears a closer resemblance to heavenly than human qualities.

"This faculty of thought, therefore, like a good husbandman who works his field, will cultivate the mind until it grows a thousand pleasures and thereby render it much dearer than the body, just as it is more excellent. If it lies indolent and dull, the pleasures harvested in it need not concern us; but the mind was given to the body,

I believe, for the same reason that salt is spread on pork, namely, to keep it from spoiling,—as those men spoil, in fact, who are not lovers. For one who does not love is pleased with nothing, and one who is pleased with nothing thinks of nothing; therefore thought lies asleep in him. But the contrary is true of lovers; for whoever is in love is pleased with what he loves, and every man thinks willingly and often of the thing which pleases him. We may conclude, therefore, that the pleasures of thought belong to lovers, not to other men. I shall not tell you how many of these pleasures there may be, for I could no more count them than enumerate the stars in heaven; yet if we would study a few of them directly, how great is the delight some gentle lover feels when thought enables him, however far from her, to reach his lady in a moment and to admire all her charming members, which he examines one by one! how great when turning to her goodly nature, he recalls her sweetness, her courtesy, her pretty ways, her wisdom, her moral virtue, and her mind with all its worthy parts!

"O Love, may I forever bless the hand with which you have drawn and written in my soul so many features of my lady. On one long canvas I always bear with me an endless line of her fair portraits rather than a single face, and ever read and reread one tall book filled with her words and accents, and in brief compass recognize, whenever I return to them, a thousand lovely traits of her and of her worth, so many of them sweet and dear to me that in my thought I feel no small part of that strong pleasure which, thanks to her, I felt when I was first aware of them. And even though these fancies had not so often

brought her charms to mind, I daily see a thousand places
which would help me to recall them: places she visited
for one amusement or another, which I no sooner eye
than I remind myself, 'Here my lady was on such a day';
'Here she did so and so'; 'Here she was seated and hence
passed me by'; 'From here I gazed at her.' So as I think
and walk, I murmur, now with myself and now with
Love, now with the very trees, the hillsides, and the river
banks which saw her there. And since I seem to have understood this afternoon that all of you like rhymes far
more than homely arguments, I may be permitted to use
a song which illustrates the point; for not long ago the
very places which brought to mind my lady drew the following verses from my heart and listened while I made
and sang them on my way:

Were the thought that burdens me
  Within these rhymes bestowed
  As sweetly as within my bosom nursed,
  The soul would then be free
  Of her too heavy load,
  And poems now the last would stand the first.
  Love, in filing better versed,
  Would bear with sharper bite
  On all who heard that sound;
  I, though now mid others found
  A lowly woodland bird of little force,
  Would fly on heaven's course
  Like some fair swan melodious and white,
  Winning my nest a name
  Of more nobility and greater fame.

But on the threshold of
    That hardy enterprise
    The stars refused to let my fancy cleave
So far, lest what with love
And my beloved's replies,
    No other man might more than I achieve.
    Though I would now relieve
    My thought, that harmony
    Is far too sweet to tell;
    And it still seems to quell
    The heart when words have hardly yet begun.
    Snow ravaged by the sun
    Is not more quickly gone than I must be,
    Enduring ceaseless rout
    Like one whose very being lives in doubt.
O harsh, malignant law:
    If I am forced to write
    That I may live, who holds me with this chain?
    If she would skyward draw
    Me in my own despite,
    Who makes my style so languid and mundane?
    High walls and towers wane
    Though solid was their plot;
    But never will I tire
    Or lessen my desire
    To satisfy that long-unfurnished need
    You gave but did not feed,
    O Love: the arrows were so keen and hot
    With which you plied my heart,
    Making her eyes the inlets of your art.
How much better it would be,

And for your greater praise,
Had I the skill to picture her complete.
As in some glass men see
Reflected color blaze
And in another part its hue repeat,
So on this glowing sheet
Would shine for other eyes
The happiness I hide;
And though it later died,
That never could our lonely flight control
From pole to spinning pole:—
Things that to your loss in silence I disguise,
And which if I could tell,
The world once more would harken to their spell.
Perhaps you would allay
A thousand kinds of care
And cast your ancient infamy aside,
That sometimes one would say,
"O faithful, loving pair,
How many pleasing thoughts your life supplied";
Another, "These were tied
By lucky knots if they
When freed, their peace obtain."
But though Love's nothing fain,
Do you my longings hear, O hillsides bright
And rock whose every height
Has breathed of sweet desires since the day
My lady up and down
Among you wandered safe in tress and gown.
If honest prayers commend
Me to your sympathy,

O beech, long partner of my past delight,
Let pity draw and bend
You now to speak to me
And move you through a certain inward sight
Which comprehends my plight,
That though another bind
And rifle me of skill,
I may one wish fulfill
Of many which the tempest hears and mocks—
So never may green locks
Be absent from your brow, nor from your rind
Some lively verse well-knit
Which in your shade may still be read or writ.
Long have you been aware
How with their starry fire
Her saintly eyes bewitched celestial powers,
And how her golden hair,
Escaping from its tire
And casting perfumes through the farthest bowers,
Filled all the grass with flowers.
And you know how her song
Made waters to their fountains
Backward run and lofty mountains
Lose their woods, which leaving all the heights around,
Descended to the sound;
Wild beasts behind and close beside her throng,
And harmless feathered things
Hang watchful overhead on steadied wings.
Shady banks with waves below,
Waters chill which roll in measure,
Meadows green providing floral gaiety,—

Who will ever hear or know
The ways she gave you pleasure,
Yet not in one great fervor glow with me?
Who otherwise will see
Her footstep's soft return,
Her winning favors bright,
And that celestial light
Which darts its rays as from the noonday sun
Upon my midnights dun?—
That light whose splendor scanning hard, I learn
To hold my fate in scorn
And climb the skyward track which few have worn.
When have you seen so much
That one fair life supplies,
Her worth, her courtesy, her virtue too?
When have you burned with such
A zeal for beauty's eyes?
(Yet love, I know, has never slept in you.)
Who guides me where her shoe
Has printed out its charms?
Who shows me grassy places
Still harboring the traces
Of that white hand which wove the subtle noose
I never seek to loose,
And of that body and those very arms
Which clasp my life so tight
That I may die, yet never ask respite?
Folk to whom on liquid feet
Here steals the winding rill,
While there the mountain thrusts its rugged head:
Were I to find retreat

As shepherd of this hill
Or warden of these woods around us spread,
At break of morning red
I would walk far and wide
To seek untroubled ease,
Bending my pious knees
Wherever quiet skies were most serene
And bowers shady green;
There would I have old error rectified
While I still kissed the ground,
My guerdon for a thousand heartaches found.
You fail to soothe me, song, yet have no blame
If here among these boughs,
Hid far from men, you are content to house.

"Not only do the places which received our ladies once, or those which being more often visited, are wont to be their faithful memoranda, bring their forms, as I have said, to mind; but everywhere some object may be found which when the outward eye considers it, provokes the inner, through a certain sweet resemblance, to recall them likewise. To speak from my own experience, as Perottino did from his: if I, according to my wont, am on a country road, there is no green embankment by a limpid stream, no winning prospect of a lovely wood, no happy solitude or cool retreat within the shady mountain's depths, which does not force me to exclaim, 'Would that my lady now were here with me, and with Love too if, feeling insecure with me alone, she sought more company among these solitary places'; thus when my thoughts are turned to her, I joyfully talk to myself about her at great length. And after sundown, when the rising shadow of the earth steals color out of things and then removes them from our sight, I cannot scan the stars in their nocturnal silence without thinking, 'If these are governors of earth's affairs, which of them first put the sweet necessity of love on me?' or fix my eyes on the silver moon's cold face without reflecting, 'Who knows that my lady may not now be gazing on this very orb on which I gaze? or that she may not say, remembering me as I remember her, "Perhaps the eyes of my Gismondo, wherever he is standing at this moment, may turn to you, O moon, as I am turning, and in this way our eyes and thoughts converge on the same object." ' So, when my fancy, in one way now and now another, brings in my lady and our loves, I dwell with her more truly than myself.

"But why recall the thoughts aroused in distant places? Right in our city no fair lady can appear before me but I am straightway reminded of my lady's charms. No handsome lad can walk the street alone with pensive steps but I surmise, 'Perhaps he is reflecting on his lady now': a guess which soon makes me too think tenderly of mine. And if I sometimes take the air in pleasure boats and leave the city tumults far behind, I can draw near no stretch of our shore on which my lady does not seem to stroll and carol to the raucous waves while gathering shells with childlike eagerness.

"The ways by which the master faculty of thought can sweeten our minds with pleasures long-departed are far more numerous than these, nay, as many as we ourselves desire. No gap, no bridge, no gate is closed to it. No menace of the heavens, no tossing sea, no rocky barrier can hold it back. Love lends it his wings, against which no evil can prevail. And just as these restore it to past joys, so when it wishes, they carry it as readily to future pleasures, which while they lack the certitude of those which are already known, yet have this compensation: a pleasure tasted can be recalled in only one embodiment, that which it had, but a pleasure not yet realized can be imagined in a thousand forms, all dear and charming and delightful. The joys, therefore, with which we entertain ourselves in thought, whether by their variety when they are still to be or by their certitude when they have been, are as continuous and prompt on all occasions as those reported of the gods.

"Now, to return by that enchanting road on which we have come hither: if each of the three pleasures already mentioned can of itself convey such blessings as we have partly seen, how much greater, ladies, must those blessings be which are produced by all three joined in one! Alas, no other satisfaction is so sweet; and these are such indeed that hardly can the judgment grasp their nature, much less the tongue describe it to another. But yesterday when Perottino entered helter-skelter on the passions which comprise that nightmare he called love, he spent a long time running over and confusing them; so now that we likewise have entered on the blessings yielded by that ecstasy which I know love to be, I am inclined to wander, in a rambling, desultory fashion, further still.

"In this excursion we may chance upon those joys, derived from other senses, of which I proposed to say nothing; and in order that they may not in that case be offended by our neglect, or perhaps agree among themselves to shrink from us henceforth as we have shrunk from them (which God forbid since I would suffer much by it), we can conduct our discourse in the same fashion that we use when dining at our royal lady's board. For from the many kinds of food and drink there set before us, we select one or two to satisfy our appetites and only taste a bite or drop of all the others by way of honoring the feast. So now that we have satisfied ourselves by speaking of the pleasures due to thinking and the first two senses, let us, when we meet the others, taste them and bid them Godspeed. But for my own part I am not so wise that in love's banquets I can use the same temperance which I reveal in other matters every day; nor would I counsel our inexperienced bridegroom that when love puts upon the board that final course which he has not yet tasted, he, like one contented with his previous fare, should merely sample this before he let it be removed: he might repent his moderation afterwards. I cannot tell, of course, how you young beauties would advise the bride.

"But to return to our pleasures: just as the splendor of the day can be more fully understood when we have diligently marked the contrasting squalor of the night, so amorous joys may be perhaps more clearly shown if we consider for a moment the lives of those who do not love.

"To begin with, not caring to make themselves attractive since they have none to please, they do not seek to adorn their persons in any amiable way, but for the most part neglect their hair and beards and teeth and hands and feet as if they were not theirs. They dress awkwardly and ill; they live disordered, melancholy lives. They have no household, no horse, no pleasure boat, no garden which does not, like its master, seem to weep. They have no friendships or acquaintance. They are not aided by others, nor do they give their fellows aid. They draw no profit from either things or men, nor are themselves of profit. They flee all public squares, all merrymaking, and all feasts, to which, however, if necessity or their misfortune brings them, they display no usage, speech, acknowledgment, or quip, or jocularity which is not wild and boorish. They recollect neither prose nor verse. They see and hear all things indifferently. In brief, the imbecility and stupefaction of their outward lives are copies of their souls within.

"Now, if you asked them what joys or profit they derive from living day by day, they would feel amazed that you should speak in this manner and would reply that you might joke, but they drew nothing from their lives except adversity and care and toil. If, on the other hand, you were to ask the same of lovers, they would perhaps make you a different answer, such as this: 'What is this question, ladies, that you ask? Our pleasures and advantages are numberless and cannot be computed. For no sooner has love pierced us through the eyes of some fair lady than our soul, which hitherto lay powerless, arising in delight, begins likewise to feel a thought arise in it and, wheeling blissfully around the lady's form, beget the wish to please her, which in its turn becomes the source of countless joys and benefits.

" 'It is a marvelous thing to note what hidden virtues are released by this new-born desire. For not only will it send a genial warmth through every vein and lade the soul with sweetness; but it will also fire our spirits, which otherwise are spent like empty lamps, and change us out of gross, material creatures into wise and civil men. To please our ladies and acquire their love and favor, we often seek to have those qualities which we perceive to be most praised in other youths, and this in order that by winning more esteem from other men, we may find greater favor with our ladies too. Then, having in short order left all his first rusticity and hour by hour learned more gentle ways, one gives himself to arms; one trains himself to practice generosity; one by courtly services endears himself to some great prince or mighty lord; one as a citizen distinguishes himself in the august employments of his country, spending what time he can in courtesy; one turns his thought to literary studies and, reading ancient histories, improves himself by imitation of those models, or entering philosophy's broad ground, like some young tree in springtime grows day by day in virtuous discipline, or even steals into the pleasant meadowland of poetry, where singing in now this and now another mode, he weaves his lady garlands of sweet flowers; one, finally, endowed with richer talents or moved by loftier affection, adorns himself with various accomplishments, arms, letters, courtesy, and all the rest which meet with praise, until, clothed in their mingled glory as in a rainbow of a thousand hues, he shows his splendor to the world.

" 'Thus while each lover exerts himself to win the favor of a single lady, he makes all men regard him, and that highly, for his worth. But if love's spur had not incited him, he might not have been known by any man or, to speak more truly, might not have known himself. What no master's switch, no father's threat, no flattery or prize, no art or toil or ingenuity or teaching could perform, love often does with grateful ease. And certainly these fruits which love imparts to us are full and sweet and endlessly diverse as well; for as the ways of lovers are not all one but many, so our rewards are not of any single kind but infinite in their variety.

" 'There are some who love only one another's honor, pure and unalloyed, and from observing their desire's lofty pitch reap such a harvest as none but the receiver can appraise. Some whose more ardent flame removes all contradiction from their loves deny each other nothing, but what one wishes the other in the same breath and fervor does; and thus, their two souls governed by a single rein, they take their happy course toward all possible delight. Some who are placed between these types of bliss, now honoring the lady's reticence, now gathering the benefits of more familiarity, and tempering one's pungent flavor with the other's sweet, compound a dish so exquisite that they never feel the least amazement or desire for another.

" 'Moreover, some shy young virgin takes unequaled pleasure in the gallantries and salutations of the lover she has just accepted. He also blesses the letter written by that darling hand which he has never touched, and reads there, not her writing, but her voice, her features, and her heart. Another youth is wafted on a sea of joy by ten small words his lady quavers forth. To many who have loved and dearly worshipped women from their childhood on, now at the very height of their affection they are vouchsafed by Heaven as their wives, the worthiest crown of men's desires. And there are other loving pairs who, having spent their warmer years in wildness and reserve, one writing, the other reading, and both enjoying only the reputation of their love, having at last, when the snow about their brows removed all diffidence, sat down and talked together, recalling their old flame with pleasure, now in tranquillity live out the sweet remainder of their days and grow each hour more contented with the time so passed.

" 'But why should we continue to discuss the good fortune of so many couples when a long history might easily be told of each? For what a pleasure to survey that forehead which displays her thoughts as pure and naked as they issue from her heart! to scan that pearl and coral, more precious than all the jewels of the East, and hear her say those words which the attentive soul receives so willingly! to gaze then in a silence sweeter than the fullest utterance, while eyes convey those messages which only love can prompt or understand! to clasp our bosoms and feel such sweetness flood them that manna seems to run throughout the heart and marrow! But let us pass over the other pleasures, dear and numerous as they may be, of which we need only say that since our lives are such as nature fashioned them when we came here, surely our sweetest course is to accept her will and govern them by the same law which the ancients made for feasts: drink or depart.

" 'Imagine, furthermore, what satisfaction and what peace of mind we gain from telling one another all that has happened to us, each accident, each lucky chance, each misadventure, each injury, each pleasure, using that freedom in our words which others hardly know when speaking only to themselves! what comfort in withholding nothing from our fellow soul and knowing that she too has hidden nothing! in sharing every hope, delight, desire! in shunning no fatigue or burden for her sake which everyone would shoulder for himself! in bearing every sort of good or ill with sweetness, no readier to live than with a happy face to die for one another! all which make our good fortune more advantageous and our ill fortune less adverse, for prosperity is doubled when it gladdens one with the pleasure of the other, and hardship, when at once shared half and half as brothers do, already loses half its power; nay, what with comfort, aid, and counsel, it melts away like snow beneath the first sunbeams, or at least we may conceal it in the shadow of new pleasures and drown it in oblivion so deep that it can hardly seem to have existed.

" 'Musicians say that when two lutes are tuned in harmony and one is touched with the other placed before it, both instruments respond, and the same note is sounded both on the one which has been touched and on the one which is untouched. O Love, what lutes or lyres respond to one another with more sympathy than two of your enamored souls? Not only do both lovers feel as one when some emergency finds them together, but even far apart, when neither has been deeply moved, they feel the sweetest and most true concent. The distant lover thinks willingly of his dear lady when he can, and hears and sees her in his thought; nor does she ever turn her mind more joyfully to anything than him; and each is sure that what one does the other does likewise. Therefore we have reason to wonder why Laodamia should need a painted figurine of wax to show her how Protesilaus looked afar.

" 'Thus, ladies, whether distant or at hand, we always find endearments and delight; for as the sun, although he moves along the Zodiac, still shines brightly down on men, so Love, although he sometimes shifts with us to other lands, yet always makes us feel his benefits in every place. On mountaintops and plains, on land and sea, in port and safety, in danger and misfortune, like health itself he ever affords both men and women his pleasures and assistance. In jagged caves and squalid huts he cheers rude shepherds in their longing; among the gilded chambers of their palaces he comforts pensive kings. He calms the anxious minds of judges; he rescues warriors from toil and, mingling nature's gay pleasantry with mankind's iron laws, brings peaceful innocence amid the bloody skirmishes of war. He nurtures youth, supports those more advanced in years, delights them both, and often does what seems a miracle, for he transfers the vigor of young plants to ancient trunks and teaches a thousand wrinkled thoughts to grow betimes under some pretty golden scalp. He cheers the virtuous, delights the wise, is good for all. He exiles sadness, casts melancholy out, removes affright, composes discord, fosters marriage, and makes our families large. He teaches us to speak, keep silence, practice courtesy. He makes departure sweet because it gives the coming back and later residence a dearer joy, and even the thought of these will make our longest separations easy to endure.

" 'He brings delightful days, when two suns shine on us, but nights still happier since they do not always rob us of our sun; and when they do, our courteous sleep is apt to bring the very happiness our vigils are denied, so that we each gaze on the other, talk together, construe our reasons, and take each other's hand, like those who experience such things by some more literal means. Each day our pleasures grow, each night our ecstasies increase, nor are the earlier diminished by those that take their place; nay, as the shining snow remains in greater purity and loveliness when shining snow has covered it, the first caresses of our love stay sweeter being laid beneath the sweetness of the last. Nor do our new endearments ever lessen or grow weaker after yesterday's; nay, as one number added to another gives a greater sum than either by itself, our joys compiled together do us far more good than they could ever do apart. Alone they are enough, but married they are more. One will beget a thousand, and each of these soon bears a thousand too. In expectation they bring happiness; when not expected, luck. If easily secured, they're dear to us, but far more dear if gotten without ease; for greater triumphs mark the victories which sweaty toil has won. Gifts and thefts and winnings and rewards, reasonings and sighs and tears, quarrels and reconciliations, first and second, false and true, long-lived and brief, all things are welcome to the lover.

" 'In short, just as in spring the fields and meadows, woodlands, hillsides, valleys, mountains, streams, and lakes and all things scanned are lovely; the earth, the sea, the air, the heavens laugh; the world is filled with light and song and warmth and odors sweet;—so in love, whatever one says or does or thinks or gazes on, it is all pleasing and all dear. For every lover's soul abounds in joy, caresses, merriment, games, pleasantry, good luck, repose, and peace.' "

Gismondo could not restrain himself from saying all this in praise of love while speech and mind were warmed to it; and he was still talking when the trumpets, which announced the dancing in those royal entertainments, resounded from the palace and told that graceful company the revels had begun. So all arising, since they perceived that they should leave, Gismondo said to them, "Our lovers might have spoken these and other things to you, my ladies, if you had bidden them to let you also know what pleasures love can give. And now I must withdraw from a course of which there is still much to run; but Lavinello, on whom the final weight of these discussions falls tomorrow, will utter in my place what I have not been able to express as fully as I would—let me not say 'should,' which I well know would not suffice us."

Then Madame Berenice, who was already moving toward the palace with the others, said, "Whether or not you have sufficiently discussed this thing, Gismondo, we are quite happy to have Lavinello lead tomorrow's talk; for if we did not know that he is more temperate in his speech than you have been today, I'm not sure that I could force myself to come."

"And what have I said, madame?" interposed Gismondo. "Have I told anything which does not in reality occur? nay, rather told much less? I can only suggest that if you wish to please her, Lavinello, you should discuss what never does occur."

Then Lavinello endeavored to withdraw from his responsibility, pretending he had said enough and that he was not yet ready to offer his own opinion and, as it were, give judgment, now that two such diverse views had been set forth and so abundantly sustained by his respective friends. But this availed him nothing; for the ladies were determined he should speak, wishing to hear a discussion led by each of these three young men in turn, whom they had always held in high repute.

And when the ladies had done their worst, Gismondo would not drop the matter, but threatened, "Lavinello, either you promise us to speak, or I will have you cited before the Queen this evening; for I am disposed to learn if pacts which are sealed during the marriage celebrations she provides can be broken in this manner. And then perhaps you will have to speak in her presence, as you never imagined when you made this agreement."

"Let's not discuss it now," Lavinello answered; "while the celebrations last, all quarrels are forbidden." Yet because he feared what might happen to him, he said he would do what they wished. And at these words the comely ladies reached the festive chambers, where those young courtiers who had the revelry in hand saw them and blocked their passage until all three had taken partners for the dance; but the three young men remained among their fellows.

GLI ASOLANI
BY MASTER PIETRO BEMBO
IN WHICH LOVE IS
THE SUBJECT OF DISCOURSE

Book Three

NOT without wonder can a man observe the difficulty of fathoming the truth about questions which arise at every hour of the day. For none of all those which may infect our minds with doubt appears to be less doubtful, less likely to provoke a dispute both pro and contra, than that about which Perottino and Gismondo have argued in the first two books; and they were of the kind who promise an immediate reply to what is asked, nor did they lack the talents to contend, in one way or another, on every subject laid before them. It was this difficulty which perhaps led some of the ancient philosophers to believe that the truth of any matter cannot be known and that we can have merely a kind of opinion about whatever exists.

Although their belief was refuted by the better of contemporary schools and is not, I think, received by many now, the minds of countless men still nurse a silent grudge against nature for keeping the true marrow of things hidden from us and covered with a thousand husks of falsehood. For there are myriads who, in despair of being able to find truth in any matter, seek it in none;

and so, having abandoned the knowledge of things since they blame nature for their ignorance, they live as chance directs. Others, still more numerous if less guilty, are discouraged by the difficulty of the task; either they believe what everybody says, accepting some opinion to which, as it were, they have been carried by the waves and cling as to a rock, or they seek without effort and, being contented with whatever they discover first, will go no further. But not to waste words on the first group: they are, I think, mistaken to consider themselves men rather than animals by birth, for in rejecting the faculty which distinguishes us from animals, they deprive the mind of its purpose and strip their lives of our chief ornament. To the latter we may begin by saying that they ought not so lightly to incur the risk of swallowing another's error, when some compelled by personal affection and others bound, as it were, by their manner of life or the studies in which they have been trained are moved to speak or write on any subject as they do, and not because they believe that it is so; that sometimes, moreover, it will even happen, I do not know how, that when we are speaking and writing on a subject, we gradually convince our minds of what we say to others.

Moreover, though they seek the truth, it is not enough to seek it lightly and to be content with each first little finding. For if we ought not to believe at once what other searchers tell us, since they may be deceived, neither ought we to believe ourselves at once since we likewise may be deceived; and this all the more because the weakness of our judgment is great and it is seldom that a first opinion, one not well considered and tested by long arguments, is really sound. If to the weakness of our judgment we join the obscurity with which nature everywhere conceals the truth, these men will see there is no greater difference between themselves and those who do not seek that quality at all than there would be between one who, while sustained by hope of reaching land, would not take care to find the buoys which mark the entrance of our labyrinthine port of Venice, and one who, abandoning all hope of ever reaching it when he has been assailed by adverse winds outside, would drop the tiller and submit to the elements' control, no longer seeking either harborage or shore.

But these errors will not overcome the gentlemen and ladies who will heed my words. Nay, the more they understand how deep is the obscurity of things and how weak our judgment is to fathom them, the less will they be willing to credit others before they have diligently searched the matter for themselves or be satisfied with a brief inquiry when the truth for which they seek is fraught with doubt; and the more satisfactory their first discoveries seem, the less contented will they be, thinking that if they press beyond, they will find other things, like those already found, which will content them more. Nor will they complain, as others do, because nature has hidden from our sight what can be known; for neither does she openly display silver or gold or gems, but buries them in her arcana, within the bowels of the earth, along the rugged mountains' veins, under the sand of running streams, and in the ocean's depths. If she has thus hidden the precious ornaments of our frail mortal part, what should she do with truth, which is not only the fair embellishment but the sun, the guide, the preserver of our minds, the controller of immoderate desires, the banisher of false delights and vain alarms, the healer of our wounded thoughts, and the embattled enemy of every ill?

Things all may equally possess are held in equal scorn by all, and rarities command a far higher price. Yet though I believe many will blame me for asking women to take part in these inquiries, since it is more suitable for them to be occupied with womanish affairs than to rummage in such matters, I shall not accept the criticism. For unless it is denied that women as well as men have minds, I do not know why they any more than we should be refused the right to seek knowledge of what one ought to flee from or pursue; and these are among the most obscure questions, around which as on their axles all the sciences revolve, questions which are the targets of all our diligence and thought. If women do not occupy all their free time with those duties which are said to be proper to them, but devote their whole leisure to literary studies and these pursuits, it makes little difference what some men say about it, for sooner or later the world will praise the women for it.

But let us hear the arguments which Lavinello propounded on the third day to a larger audience than his companions found. For on the previous day, when the three ladies were sought among those with whom they were wont to linger before going to the festivities, and it had been discovered they were in the garden and the cause was known, word traveled from mouth to mouth until it reached the Queen. When she had heard what splendid things that company discussed, although none could tell her exactly what they were, the reputation of the three young men for being alert and well informed filled her with a desire to learn what their discussions were like. So in the evening, after all of them had enjoyed themselves and dined and had dessert, awaiting only what the Queen might bid them do, she turned toward Madame Berenice, who was among the nearest, and graciously inquired, "How did you like our garden this afternoon, and what can you tell us about it? for we understand that you have been there with your friends."

"It pleased us very well, madame," replied the lady, rising as she bowed. "It seemed to me to be all that a garden of Your Majesty's should be."

Then, when courtesy had said what could be said and Lisa and Sabinetta, who were not far away, had added their account, all the other ladies who had not seen the garden felt a desire to visit it and thought it would be an age before the Queen arose, if they were to go that evening while there was daylight still; for it was rapidly declining to its lair beyond Morocco. But she, who easily perceived their impatience, rejoined when Madame Berenice had spoken, "Indeed, the garden has frequently given us much pleasure; and as it is a good many days since we have been in it and these ladies would perhaps enjoy a little fresh air, we might all go there now in the cool of the evening."

So, rising and taking Madame Berenice by the hand, she descended the steps with all the others; and when she had given them permission to wander here and there for their amusement, she seated herself with her young companion beside one of those fair windows opening on the spacious plain, and said, "You have told us many things about this garden, and told them well, although we who know can see that you have overpraised it. But you have not told us anything about the discussions you held here; and while we know nothing in regard to them, we learn how bright and charming they have been. If you can give us an account of them, it will please us exceedingly."

Berenice saw no way to refuse her; and so, after praising the three young men at some length and tendering her courteous excuses since she would find it difficult even to rehearse so many and such arguments in her own mind and would be far less able to recount them to Her Majesty, she ended by briefly summarizing all that Perottino and Gismondo had said, beginning with the leadership accorded to the latter and setting forth, as well as she knew how, the questions both of them propounded, but always taking heed that she addressed a lady and a queen. When Her Majesty had listened to this explanation, considering that she had seen only the sketches of fair paintings, as it were, and that Lavinello was to speak the following day, she resolved to honor that gallant company by being present at his discourse. And the lady was overjoyed to hear her say so much, for she believed that if the Queen would come, there would be no opportunity for anyone whom the subject and place of their discussion might lead to talk in some improper way.

As Madame Berenice finished speaking, all daylight had departed from our hemisphere, and everywhere the stars had begun to take their heavenly posts; so by the light of many torches the Queen and the other ladies climbed the steps again, to seek their chambers and repose. When Madame Berenice found her two companions, she told them what Her Majesty and she had only now discussed and how she felt about it. Without delay they sent for the three young men, at whose arrival she explained to Lavinello, "The very thing with which Gismondo threatened you today has come to pass: know that tomorrow you will have to speak in the presence of the Queen our lady." And after she had made them understand how it had happened and they had discussed it for a time, the young men took their leave in order to attend to nightly tasks before their slumber.

But on the morrow, when dinner had been served and each was withdrawing to his own retreat, the Queen gathered an appropriate group of ladies and gentlemen, including our young men and women, and went with them into the garden. There she, like the others, sank on the flowered grass beneath the laurels' shade, or rather on two splendid pillows which her maidens had laid down for her; and all the gentlemen and ladies were seated too, nearer or farther off according to their quality. Then, as they awaited nothing but the words of Lavinello, he bowed toward Her Majesty and finally began:

"Madame, when I learned that you wished me to deliver a discourse in your presence which I had expected to make before our little band of the last two days, my own ineptitude, the importance of the subject, and the convenience of Your Highness all filled me for a time with doubt; and it appeared that I had made a mistake in promising our ladies and my friends to accept this responsibility. For although I then believed I could somehow satisfy their wishes, yet as soon as I thought that you would overhear my words and imagined you before me, my powers seemed much weaker and my theme much larger than I had at first supposed.

"Thus I found myself hard-pressed until my mind drew comfort from turning to the infinite kindness which is your natural endowment; and since that, as I knew, transcended all my fallibilities, I decided it could hardly be an error to obey you. Furthermore, I became aware of other considerations: as, for example, that if fortune had provided me with an auditor and judge suitable to the greatness of my subject, it ought not to make me unhappy, for you might extend your ample pardon where I erred, your generous aid where I fell short; and that, if I looked further, to have the Queen of Cyprus hear my arguments on love would be the very pledge of my success since Gismondo proposed the question and he and Perottino have disputed it without that great advantage. So may this happy augury avail me, madame, in my undertaking, and may the sweet illumination of your presence inspire me in what I have to say; for in its beneficial light my slender courage spreads its wings and, by your good leave, stirs me to begin.

"The doctrines which my companions set forth on their respective days and which our ladies explained to you last evening, madame, might be accepted and their differences willingly resolved without further consideration, were it not that since one of them is moved by the grief and the other by the joy he feels in loving, each has exceeded the proper limits in presenting his case and at the same time too narrowly limited the field of his discussion. To put in brief what they took hours to expound: one of them wished to persuade us that love is always evil and never can be good, the other that it is always good and never can be evil. But if they had simply said that it is good and that it is evil, without going further, Your Majesty might well have spared yourself the trouble of listening to me; for the love which they describe may be both good and evil, as I shall try to make clear to them. And although it must obviously be admitted that one of these opinions, as they are expressed, cannot be true since they are in disagreement, nevertheless the contenders have spread the sails of their discourse so well that their audience undoubtedly considers both opinions true, or at least that it is not easy to decide which is less true; yet this in itself is grounds for thinking both are false inasmuch as truth, when touched, immediately reveals itself to the observer by shining out like a flame from the surrounding errors.

"And surely Perottino has brought together many inventions and many arguments in order to convince us that love is always bitter, always harmful; Gismondo, on the other hand, has gathered just as many to convince us that love is never otherwise than sweet and beneficial. One has been funereal; the other festive. The tears of one have made us weep; the other's jesting has more often made us laugh. Thus each in his own way strives to support his opinion with more equivocations than his friend; and while other men dispute in order to find out a truth which is uncertain, these, with their polemics, have called in question one of which there was no doubt. But my companions must not expect me to oppose both sides of their debate, excessive as they are in general; I shall contend with them only long enough to make them realize what devious and harmful roads they follow.

"Then, madame, since love is nothing but desire which always circles round the thing which pleases it, for it is not possible to love without desiring either to enjoy what we love, or to enjoy it in some other way than we now do, or to enjoy it always, or to accomplish some good which we seek for the object of our affection; and since desire is nothing but love, for we can in no wise desire what we do not love—I would say that all love and all desire are one and the same. Furthermore, these occur in only two forms, either natural or begotten by our will. The natural desires, such as love of life, of understanding, of self-perpetuation, of children, and of useful things, are those which nature gives without intermediary, which suffer no abatement, and which are the same in all of us. Those begotten by the individual will, on the other hand, vary according to the way in which our will is moved to yearn for one or another object, now this or that, now much or little; and these desires grow less or more, are dropped or taken up again, suffice or do not meet our needs, and differ from this mind to that, as we ourselves wish and are ready to receive them there.

"But the various kinds of desire which I have noted, madame, were not conferred on us haphazardly, nay, rather by the watchful heed of One, whoever it may be, in whom we and all creation find our true First Cause. For wishing that we, like all the other creatures, might perpetuate ourselves and be restored from time to time, He saw it would be necessary to plant in us, just as in them, the aforementioned love of life, of children, of things which are useful and bring us to a better and more nearly perfect state; a love without which the first generation of our species would have been the last. But since He had created us for a greater and more lofty end than other creatures and had therefore added the rational parts of our minds, He was likewise constrained, in order that reason might not waste with inactivity, to add that will which I have described, the faculty by which we freely choose whether or not we might desire other things as we consider them of less or greater worth. Thus, in satisfying our natural and primary needs, all of us love and desire alike, as other creatures do, each striving to live and maintain himself as well as possible; but not so in the case of our other inclinations, for Perottino will hardly love the one I do, or I the one he does, or he will love her less or more than I.

"Now we must admit Gismondo's argument of yesterday, that because nature cannot be deceived, the natural desires are always equally good and never can in any way be wrong; but since our will can be deceived, and is deceived more often than I care to think, those other desires which Gismondo failed to explain may be either good or bad, according to the target set before them by the will. And such is the desire which Gismondo has proposed for our discussion, the one men commonly call love, from which we take our name of lovers: such because each of us voluntarily loves or ceases to love or differs from others in his love, and does not always love of necessity or the same object or in the same way, as happens in the case of natural desires; for this desire is good or evil according to the goal our will assigns to it. But Gismondo, in order to support his flimsy arguments, mingled natural desires with it, intending to show that it was always good and never could be harmful.

"Who can fail to see that if I love some gallant, gentle lady, and love her rather for her wit, integrity, good breeding, grace, and other qualities than for her bodily attractions, and love those attractions not for themselves but as adornments of her mind,—who can fail to see my love is good because the object of my love is likewise good? And on the other hand, if I resolve to love some loose, dishonest lady, or to love, even in one who is chaste, what causes loose, dishonest thoughts, how can such a love be anything but wicked and depraved when the thing I seek is in itself depraved? The first type of lover undoubtedly enjoys the blessings which Gismondo has ascribed to those of every kind,—an awakening of talents, a deliverance from folly, a growing sense of worth, an escape from all low desires and annoyances of life, a welcome refuge in every time and place. But the second type can be just as sure of finding only harm; he will often experience the very misadventures Perottino has told us that all kinds of lovers meet,—disdain, remorse, suspicion, jealousy, sighs, weeping, grief; the loss of all good works, time, honor, friends, instruction, life; the waste and ruin of himself.

"But you are not to think, Gismondo, that because I

speak in this way, I consider it well to love in the fashion you have described. I am as far from you as you are from the truth; and you depart from it every time you allow your desire to carry you beyond the first two senses and the faculty of thought because they fail to satisfy your love. For in the opinion of the soundest of the ancient schools, a virtuous love may be defined as a desire of beauty; and if you had used the same diligence to find out what beauty is as you displayed yesterday in the subtle delineation of your fair lady's various members, you would not love as you do now or praise the object of your love as you have done.

"Beauty is a kind of grace which is born of proportion and the harmony of things; the more nearly perfect it is in its embodiments, the more lovely it renders them to us; and in human beings it is an attribute of the mind no less than of the body. For as that body whose members are proportionate is beautiful, so is that mind whose virtues meet in harmony; and each enjoys its share of beauty according to the grace which, as I have said, informs and reconciles its parts.

"So virtuous love is a desire for beauty of mind no less than body; and in order to reach that end and object of its longing, love spreads and beats its wings. And on its flight two senses guide it: hearing, which leads it to the mind's attractions, and sight, which turns it to the body's. For as the forms which our eyes perceive reveal how fair the body is, so from the words which reach our ears we understand the fairness of the mind (indeed nature gave us speech only in order that we might reveal our minds to one another). But chance and fortune may frequently cut our desires off from these approaches to their goal since, as you have said, neither eye nor ear will serve us when we are far from what we love; therefore the same nature which provided these two senses has likewise given us the faculty of thought, with which we may enjoy both kinds of beauty when we please. By thought, as you explained so fully yesterday, we may recapture them and relish them unhindered at any hour that we wish.

"Now taste and touch and smell are no more able to reveal the body's beauty than the mind's, for these three senses are limited to more material objects than the others are. If you were to smell these flowers or run your hand among these herbs or taste them, you could tell which of them were fragrant and which rank, which jagged and which smooth, which bitter and which sweet; but unless you saw them too, you could have no more conception of their beauty than a blindman of some painted image placed before him. If virtuous love, as I have said, is the desire of beauty and we are led to beauty only by our eyes or ears or thoughts, all that lovers seek with their other senses, unless they seek it in order to nourish life, is evil and not virtuous love; and you, Gismondo, in pursuing it love ugly things, not beauty. For it is monstrous to go in search of pleasures which are in another's jurisdiction and cannot be enjoyed without usurping them, pleasures difficult in themselves as well as harmful, dirty, and profane; while those might be enjoyed which lie within our power, which can be had without another's loss, and which are easy, harmless, clean, and holy.

"It would have been sufficient yesterday, Gismondo,

to have praised the latter; those you may always commend, in prose as well as poetry, since they undoubtedly can never be too much commended. But if you wished to discuss these others, it should have been with all the blame and odium you could; thus virtuous love would have received its fitting praise, whereas you have reviled it most unfittingly. And since Love is called a mighty god, I would encourage you to amend your error by doing the very opposite of Stesichorus in antiquity; for when he had been blinded for scolding Helen in his verses, he won his sight back by making other verses in her honor. Contrariwise, today you should as much disparage these three senses as you contrived to praise them yesterday; and so you would regain the intellectual sight which you have lost."

When Lavinello had reached this point, he fell silent for a little, gathering strength to continue, as one is apt to do in such a matter. Then the Queen, who had quietly drawn herself together, began to speak in all serenity: "You have done well, Lavinello, to remind us, when you mention poets and their verses, of something which the very amenity of your discourse might otherwise have led us to forget. For your companions, as we understand, mingled their recent arguments with the charming poems which your ladies heard them say; and since we have not heard their poems, wouldn't you like to mingle the present argument with some of yours, to which we also might be privileged to listen?"

"Madame," answered Lavinello with a deferential bow, "were my poems as much more charming than my friends' as you are greater than our ladies, I might not be accused of arrogance if I recited one of mine today as they did many of their rhymes before. But mine, being far beneath the notice of our little circle, have even less desire to be heard in any theater as ample as your presence gives. May it please Your Majesty then not to burden my shoulders with a weight I cannot carry."

"Your great politeness does us too much honor," replied the Queen; "and it may well annoy your ladies, whom we regard as sisters. But to let that pass: you would do us an injury indeed if you were unwilling to amuse us in the same way as your friends amused their listeners, especially when we are told that you too are a fertile and ingenious poet."

So Lavinello found no way that he could honestly refuse her; and after he had heard both Berenice, whom the Queen graciously begged to make him speak at least one song, and Gismondo, who said he was a master of the art, he finally agreed: "Because Your Majesty desires it, I will recite for you as well as I am able; and since you ask me to do so now that I am discussing the three innocent kinds of pleasure which are felt in virtuous love, I will tell you what I have already written of them in three songs which were born, as it were, together. Thus, having crossed this dangerous pass, I may complete the rest of my discourse with more assurance." Which said, he then began the first:

Though pleasure would impassion me to write
   And Love's own hand provide the needed art,
   From neither do I dare to summon aid;
   Put them and every other wish to flight.
   May this reward alone impel my heart

To speak and in contentment be repaid:
To seem to have so fair a face displayed
Before me, such high thoughts, and words so pure
That though I must abjure
All hope, by force of wit or other skill,
Of bringing things to view
As I have felt them, beautiful and new,
Gifts which a thousand years could not fulfill,—
Yet these, my stars coerce
Me now and then to stammer forth in verse.
That early time when first the hoarfrost yields
To violets and, varying its part,
The sun must now its sullen mask forswear,
Between the limpid sky and tender fields
My gentle lady stole within my heart,
Who need no more than once have stolen there.
My luck would have it that her golden hair
Was then untied, and her enchanting eyes
Had in such happy guise
Addressed their gracious, light, belated gaze
That calling them to mind,
All that had seemed among us most designed
For rarer charm I rated false displays
And gave myself this cheer:
"Love surely may be found not far from here."
And truly said; as daylight with the sun,
So Love forever with my lady goes,
From whose belgards he never ranges wide.
I heard her, while she granted words to one,
In such melodious cadence sound their close
As hardly seemed to human tongue allied.

A silver fountain babbled by her side,
Which saw its swollen waters overflow
Banks found that day too low,
Saw every branch her saintly glances meet
Through all the forest round
More foliage grow and bow toward the ground,
And flowers tinge the grass beneath her feet;
And when her accents filled
My ravished ear, the very winds were stilled.
All the felicities which lovers sure
Had never yet until that morning found
Were wholly mine, though she was hardly seen.
Down to her feet her garment flowed more pure
Than snow; the hem's encircling whiteness round
Might well have made the air it swept serene.
Her walk would rescue souls from torments keen
And remedy each long-unmended breach;
But her sagacious speech,
Whose sweetness clove me from myself, her eyes
Then shining clear, her hair,
Which served to bind the burden of my care,
Descended all, it seemed, from Paradise
To earth, that they might store
The world with peace and empty it of war.
"Alas: if destiny decide that these
Are merely human words and woman's beauty,
The man is blest who hears her and beholds;
But otherwise, what pinions shall I seize
To follow her if she concede no duty
To linger where a lover sighs and scolds?"
So thought I; and as for what the sight enfolds,

I noted one who now her face portrayed
Within my soul and made
Her phrases now invoke my inner ear,
"These wings," avowing low,
"You always have, wherever you would go."
I shook myself, and just as I am here,
So was my lady fair
Both seen and heard within my bosom there.
Stay by me, song, if you with all my great
Celestial wealth for aid
Would still go forth so beggarly arrayed.

The poem ended, Lavinello would have returned to his discourse; but the Queen, who had not forgotten his remark about three songs which had been born together, was so pleased with the first of them that she desired him to say the other two. So he began the second in these words:

That this unmeasured yearning should ensnare
My soul in its first wish, and to its wings
Have all their skill in lifting me denied,
Can cause no wonder: from wood so rare
The flames rise upward and the longing springs
To praise your virtues, lady, far and wide.
Your dwelling is within; what shines outside
Can be no other than your afterglow.
But though I hardly show
Your rays in these unskillful rhymes I stitch,
In you is surely seated
The root of all that is through me repeated.
The words are destitute and weak with which

I would, if they were stout,
Make many a well-bred lover more devout.
Yet from the very day that I first raised
Your royal seat within my heart, the whole
Of my existence was a joy to me.
If truth may be through lengthy trial appraised,
Whether the dead or living claim my soul,
I hope to dwell among them happily:
So sure a foot has my felicity.
Nay, and beneath the circle of the moon
There is no higher boon,
No fortune more beatified than mine.
If other men are glad
One moment, agony soon drives them mad;
But me from gracious festivals divine
No grief will ever pluck,
Thanks to your kindness, lady, and my luck.
And if grim destiny should some day cleave
Me with still greater strokes (it cannot miss
The body under which I sink and wane),
The zest with which Love arms me will receive
The blow nor suffer it to harm the bliss
Beyond, where you who make it bliss, remain.
Yet by myself I never shall attain
The age when other mortals re-embark;
Sure I was born the mark
For every arrow shot by human ill.
But you have been my shield;
And though it be my quality to yield,
Not much of me submits to fortune still.
Alas, who can reveal

The many fashions of the joy I feel?
For often one rotation of your eyes,
 One word to mollify the tortured nerves,
 Affords my heart a happiness so rare
 As neither tongue nor writing could comprise;
 No myrtle bush or bay its leaves preserves
 So well as these their every winning air.
 And I am so accustomed to this fare
 My soul cannot be pleased or led askew
 By that which is not you
 Or which the thought of you has not aneled:
 Both when the briefest day
 Sees snowdrifts hide each bank and rising brae
 And when the longest burns the open field,
 When blossoms first unfold
 And when the leaves grow fewer, being old.
Scanning your lovely countenance, I find
 Acanthus, lily, violet, and rose,
 Sapphire and ruby veined with pearl and gold;
 Hearing your daily voice, I have divined
 A harmony that gentle airs disclose
 And sweet angelic choruses unfold;
 All other joys, were they together rolled
 And placed beside that pleasure which the thought
 Of you supplies, were naught.
 Nor would I swear that Love so much relied
 Upon his torch and bow
 As on the royal largesse you bestow;
 For now he seems to flit in jaunty pride
 Before you and pretend,
 "I'm mighty since this woman is my friend."

O song, you would from other bivouacs
  Than mine remain afar
  If you discerned how barbarous you are.

From this poem Lavinello at once proceeded to the third:

Since Love is not too weary to exhort
  Me that my text, as always, should be she,
  And pleasure more than ever so advises,
  I shall go forward; and if my words fall short
  Of truth, yet may my lady pardon me
  Though all our usages she little prizes.
  How should I climb aloft where she arises
  If heavy I and low, she high and light?
  Enough that day and night
  My bending spirit does her praises frame,
  And when the fervent mind
  Enforces me, I carve some smoother rind,
  Or sands more faithful, with her gracious name,
  That seas may speak thereof
  And all the forest welcome her with love.
Thus might I partly sate my fond desire
  To rise, by praising her, above the earth;
  But fear of falling draws the reins too straight,
  And ever finding reasons to admire
  Still more that steadfast pillar of great worth,
  I never can the sum of them relate.
  Yet that men may discern the quiet state
  Of which she is the cause and sole delight,
  Sometimes I needs must write
  As each conceit is harvested by thought:

Whether that silver voice
Whose sound unlocks and makes my heart rejoice,
Or you, dear eyes of shining starlight wrought,
Who are my remedy,
Except when you deny yourselves to me.
You are my only port on friendless seas:
  As sun replenishes the world with light
And winds compel the clouds to fly with fear,
So you procure my comfort and great ease
And your appearance causes my despite
And grief on every part to disappear.
Again, when I my lady's accents hear,
They draw me back from all disgraceful broils
And free me from those toils
Which tether and incline our souls to earth;
So that I firmly trust,
When I escape this prison-house of dust,
Death I may rob of an undying worth
And in a fairer form
Remain the lovers' paradigm and norm.
My third delight is that I am allowed
  In lofty contemplation to repeat
The charms I view unwearied though alone;
There I perceive her port demure yet proud,
Her laughter which makes every torment sweet,
Her singing which might captivate a stone.
How many things which silence leaves unknown
My heart in close enjoyment holds confined.
So, to confirm my mind,
In gardens ever rife with flowers new
I hear the grass aver,

"Your lady has this gift reserved to her:
To make it summer here and winter too."
I with such fancies ply
Myself nor can with others satisfy.
Whoever does not know how Paradise
And all its souls rejoice to see the Lord,
Let him explore the pleasure I commend.
From that day forth he need not fear that ice
Or heat or other outrage life has stored
Will ever dare draw near him or offend.
Nay, should my lady only slightly bend
Her gracious brow to give him her Godspeed,
He will no longer need
Our guidance, being one to conquer fate.
For those alluring eyes
Will call on him to overleap the skies;
They will disclose a thoroughfare so straight
That he may spread his wings,
Transcending in his flight all human things.
Whither away, my song, if still with me
Your two companions stay?
Sure you have not more wealth or skill than they.

When the three songs had been despatched, Lavinello
resumed his original discussion in these terms: "Madame,
the little I have uttered hitherto might well suffice to
show our ladies the falsehood which both of my companions, as you have heard, so cleverly concealed within
the many folds of their recent arguments; but it would
not reveal that fraud to you or to the girl who sang so
winningly before the table of Your Majesty two days

ago and therewith appointed me my course, while my companions have followed in the footsteps of the other two.

"Yet in this matter my great need has been undoubtedly well served by fortune. For early this morning, when I had parted from my friends and left the castle in order to pursue my thoughts alone, taking a path which climbs the slope behind us, without knowing where I went, I reached the little grove which crowns the charming mountaintop as if it had been planted there by careful measurement. The scene did not displease me; nay, forgetting love while I stopped to admire the beauty of that plantation from without, I was tempted by its silvan quietude and shade to enter it and finally chose an almost invisible trail which after branching from the pathway, led my steps within; nor did I stop before my slender track had brought me to a little clearing. At one of its corners, I became aware, a hut was built, and not far off there slowly moved among the trees a solitary figure, a bearded, white-haired man clothed in a material like the bark of the young oaks surrounding him. He had not perceived me; and deep in thought, as it seemed, he sometimes stopped in his perambulation and after a little began pacing very slowly again.

"He had done this many times when it struck me that he must be that holy man who I had heard was living as a hermit in this neighborhood, to which he had come in order that he might, by studying sacred books, the better pursue his lofty contemplations. If he were the one I thought, I would therefore have willingly stepped forward to greet him and to seek his advice in regard to my discourse, remembering as I did my responsibility to speak before Your Majesty today; for I had heard that he was very well informed and that for all the discomforts of a saintly life, supported in solitude on a diet of wild berries, roots, and water, he was quite affable and ever gave a soft, benevolent reply to any question that another wished to ask. But since it appeared uncivil to drag him out of his reflections, I stood gazing in expectancy; and hardly had I done so when he turned in my direction and seeing me, provided the opportunity I wished. Approaching, I saluted him with deep respect. For a moment he remained suspended in thought, then moved toward me with a brisker step, saying, 'So, my Lavinello, you are here even now.' And with this he drew near and gently took me by both cheeks, kissing my forehead.

"It was a new experience indeed for me to be so familiarly received and named by one with whom I had no acquaintance and no way of knowing how he came by his with me. Surprised and half-shamefully studying the holy man to see if I could recognize him as one whom I had met before, yet failing to identify him, I stood silent for some time, until a tender smile revealed his perception of my wonder. Whereupon I found the courage to reply, 'Here indeed, father, is Lavinello as you say, come I know not whether by chance or Heaven's will. But you make him marvel exceedingly since he cannot understand how you came to know one who never was in this place before and who, as far as he can tell, has never yet seen you.'

"Then the good old man, who had already taken me

by the hand and was moving toward the hut, replied with a happy, tranquil countenance, 'Lavinello, I do not wish you to marvel at what may highly please you. But because you seem to me to be delicate and are likely to have tired yourself in climbing up here from the castle on foot, let us go over there so that you may sit down; and I will gladly keep you company, though I am not the most amusing man in the world, and while you rest, I will tell what I know of you.'

"Having led me, through a few openings, to some broom plants which grew before the little house, he seated himself on a tree trunk which was placed along them and served as a rude kind of bench for him and his guests. Here he invited me to sit and when I had rested for a little, began: 'So wide and deep, my son, is the ocean of God's providence that our humanity can find no limit when setting forth upon it and cannot rest midway; for the sail of our mortal wit cannot carry us to its bounds, and the rope of our judgment, however lengthy, cannot reach to its bottom, so that though many things are seen to happen every day in accordance with its wish and plan, we do not know why or how they happen. And this is now apparent in my recognizing you, which causes you to wonder.'

"He proceeded to tell me that while he slept last night, he had a dream in which he saw me come to him just as I later came; and that when I had told him who I was and recounted all the accidents of the past two days, our controversy, my duty to speak at this hour in Your Majesty's presence, and part of what I intended to say, that part, that is, which you have just heard, I seemed to ask what he believed and what he would say on this subject if he, like me, were obligated to discuss it. At this fancy he had roused himself and thought the matter over for some time, and was still considering it when I arrived; and thus he had received me as one known, with whom the night had already made him familiar.

"My previous wonder grew a hundredfold while I was listening to him, and my belief in his saintliness increased exceedingly. So when he had spoken, 'Father,' I said with fear and reverence, 'I see that I have not come hither without the gods' desire, to whom it is evident that you are dear. Now they have already shown, by sending you your vision, that they are pleased to have you lend your aid and counsel in my overwhelming need, in order that our Queen, their well-beloved, may receive such honor as they wish to her, not, I believe, as I can give. May you be pleased, therefore, to satisfy their will, since I ought now to say no more of mine.'

" 'Nay rather, may it please One whom all good actions please, to let me satisfy your wish together with His will,' he answered.

"And having answered, he raised his eyes to heaven, for a little fixed his attention there, then turned to me again as he went on: 'Now, Lavinello, you are as dear to me as any son; and I can tell you that you and your friends have put a real burden on your shoulders in engaging to speak of love and its condition, not only because a multitude of things can be said about it, but even more because everybody discusses it all the time, giving it qualities which do not belong to it and omitting or discounting those which are most proper and necessary, a circumstance which makes it more difficult for us to discover the truth about it since we must, as it were, sail against the current of other men's opinions. Yet none ought then to be discouraged from the search or cease to strive because it is so wearisome to reach his goal; for there are few if any other things of which we should be more desirous to gather knowledge than of love. Which of you, in the talks your friends have already given and in that which you expect to give, is more successful in finding such an understanding, which less, I leave to the judgment of my lady Queen; but you deserve much praise for daring to pursue it.

" 'Nevertheless, if you would have me add something to the rest and carry the search a little farther, so be it, provided you do not assume that the truth is more apt to be hidden under these broom plants than elsewhere. And that you may not continue to believe, as you have said, that love and desire are the same, I shall venture to tell you that this is not true. But to begin with, let us see what in us, or what part of us, love is; and afterward I will show you that it is not desire.

" 'It is well-known, then, that the intellectual part of our souls has three divisions, or qualities, or distinct species: first there is the intellect itself, the part which is fitted and ready for understanding but may, however, be deceived; then there is the understanding, which is not always operative since intelligible things are not always understood, nay, which the intellect enjoys only when it receives some profit from considering what it is invited to understand or know; and finally there arises out of these the thing, whether we wish to call it light or semblance or truth, which when we understand it well, is found to be the fruit and offspring of the other two, but which misunderstood may properly be called neither truth nor semblance nor light, but rather night and falsehood. So, in precisely the same way, the volitional part of our souls has three distinct divisions, each with its proper functions: first there is the will power itself, which may be either willing or unwilling and is the fountainhead of both the others; then there is the desire of which I speak, by whose agency this will is brought into play, whether much or little or even negatively when we are unwilling; and finally these two beget the third, which being pleased is spoken of as love, and when displeased must of necessity be known as hate.

" 'Love therefore, Lavinello, is born and grows as you have seen, and is that part in us which you believe; yet now you may also see that it is not desire. For while we can desire nothing without loving it, it does not follow that we can love nothing without desiring it; indeed there are many things we love without desiring, that is, all those which we possess. As soon as we possess a thing, we lose all desire for that part of it which lies in our possession, replacing that feeling with pleasure. A man does not desire what he has, but rather he delights in its enjoyment; and still he loves it far more dearly than at first. To take your own case: while you were still a tyro in the art of writing verses, you loved it for its charm and beauty, and you desired to possess it too; now, having learned its use, you desire it no longer, but derive only pleasure from your skill and love the art much more than when you still did not possess it.

" 'The truth of this will be more evident to you if, in the same way, you consider the nature of hate and fear. For though we can fear nothing without hating it, yet there are times when we hate a thing without fearing it. For example, you may hate the violators of another's wife and yet feel no fear of them since you yourself have no wife to be violated; and I may hate the robbers of another's goods, yet without being afraid of them since, as you see, I have no wealth for which to fear. It follows, then, that as we may have hate without fear, so we may have love without desire; and therefore love is not desire but another thing.

" 'Yet, Lavinello, I would not reason or dispute with you as closely as with school philosophers; and I am willing, if you wish, to call love and desire the same thing. But since you told me last night that love might be either good or evil according to the objects and the scope assigned to it, I would like to know from you why lovers are sometimes attracted to evil and unworthy objects? Is it because they in loving follow their senses rather than their reason?'

" 'I think, father, it is for no other cause,' I answered.

" 'Now if I were to ask you why, on the contrary, lovers also desire fit and salutary objects,' the holy man continued, 'would you not reply that in loving these they follow the dictates of reason rather than of sense?'

" 'Such and no otherwise would be my reply.'

" 'It is good, therefore, when men follow reason rather than sense, and evil, on the other hand, when they follow sense rather than reason?'

" 'Undoubtedly.'

" 'Now tell me,' he went on, 'why it is evil for men to follow sense rather than reason.'

" 'Because they forgo the better part, which is reason, and abandon what is surely theirs, in order to grasp the worser, which is sense, and follow what is not properly theirs.'

" 'I'll not deny,' he said, 'that reason is a better thing than sense; but how can you say that sense does not belong to men? Don't they use their senses?'

" 'Now you are testing my powers of perception, father. Nevertheless I'll give you an obedient reply:—Just as the first and lowest step in every staircase has none beneath it, but the second has the first, and the third has both of them, and the fourth has all three, so it happens in all the things which God has created, from the lowest up to man. For some of them simply exist, as, for example, stones and this dead wood on which we are seated; others, such as all the plants and grasses, both exist and live; others again, the wild animals, exist and live and use their senses; and still others, namely we ourselves, exist and live and use both sense and reason. But each is said to have as more peculiarly his own the thing of which another has less. While the plants both exist and live, only life is said to belong to them since they share existence with the stones and many other things which do not have life; and though existence and life and sense all belong equally to the animals, as we have seen, nevertheless they are said to have sense alone because they have life in common with the plants and existence in common with the plants and the stones, which are yet without sense. In the same way, the fact that we exist and live and have sense and use reason cannot be said to mean that existence or life or sense is properly ours, for they are attributes of the other three and therefore not peculiar to ourselves; but reason can be called our own since the three orders of creatures below us enjoy no part in it.'

" 'If reason is proper to men and sense to animals,' said the holy man, 'and if reason, as there is no doubt, is a more perfect thing than sense, then those who follow reason in their love act like men in following the more perfect thing; and those who follow sense act like animals in following the less perfect.'

" 'Sense, as you have said, father, would surely lie, not on the human, but on the animal side.'

" 'Then can we as lovers,' he pursued, 'abandon the better part which is our own, in order to grasp the worse which is another's?'

" 'Indeed we can.'

" 'But how is that possible?'

" 'Because the will, which allows us to do or not to do it, is a matter of our free choice and not constrained to follow one thing rather than another.'

" 'But can the wild creatures too forgo the better part, the one which is properly theirs?'

" 'No, I would say that they cannot forgo it unless compelled to do so by some external force; for not free will, but only appetite is given them, which when attracted by the things they perceive outside themselves, will always respond to sense. So when a horse feels thirsty, he will move toward the first water he can see, and bend to drink unless prevented by his bridle.'

· 177 ·

" 'How I wish, Lavinello, that you had been able to answer otherwise; for if we in our loves can lose the better part through grasping for the worse and animals cannot do so, since they never act like plants although we act like animals, our state would seem to be far worse than theirs, and this free will of ours of which you speak would, in that case, have been bestowed upon us for our harm. Nature, we might almost think, repented having made so many steps on that staircase you describe; and since she had endowed us with the advantage of reason, which she could not retract, she also gave us this freedom of choice in order that we might voluntarily withdraw from our step and descend to that of the animals: just as Phoebus, when he had made a prophetess of the Trojan girl Cassandra and could not revoke what he had done though he repented of it, further provided that none should believe her prophecies. But what do you think? does it seem to be as I have said?'

" 'Father, I hardly know how to say what I think or do not think, except that I share all your opinions. Yet would you have me believe that nature, which cannot err, can repent of her acts?'

" 'Nay, I would never have you believe that,' the holy man replied. 'My son, I would rather have you consider that nature, which it is true can never err, would not have granted our will the power to be misled by sense and to sink to the level of the species below us if she had not likewise given us the power to follow reason and to raise ourselves to that which is above us. For she would have been unjust if she had necessarily and forever bestowed her privileges on those things which she created for our use and sustentation, while we, the masters of them all, were given a free choice merely that we might risk the eternal loss of the capital with which she had endowed us, but never might increase it. Nor is it credible that she would have granted us a free and easy inclination to all those tender, overpowering charms with which our senses drown the mind at every hour, in every place and state, so that by descending to our appetites we may become uncleanly beasts, and yet should have denied us the ability to rise to those other charms with which our intellect allures us to use our reason and become, by striving upward, gods.

" 'O Lavinello, what do you think is this eternal orb of the sun before you, which ever shines so steadily, so surely, with such unwearied radiance? or that other sister light which never is the same? or all the splendors which we see everywhere borne on that marvelous and most divine of spheres, turning around us and revealing now these beauties and now those? They, my son, are none other than His charms who apportions these, as well as everything besides, and sends them as His messengers inviting us to love Him. For wise men say that of our two constituents we take the body, that fleeting, inharmonious mixture of water, fire, earth, and air, from our progenitors, but take the pure, immortal soul from Him whom it desires to rejoin.

" 'But since the soul is imprisoned in the body for many years during which it sees no light and may forget its divine origin, while it sleeps in us as children and then while it is overwhelmed with youthful desires, losing itself in earthly loves, He recalls it by showing us each day the sun, each night the stars, and in its proper turn the moon. What is this spectacle if not a kind of voice which calls us unremittingly: "Why beat the air, you fools? In your blind preoccupation with your false beauties, you like Narcissus feed yourselves on vain desire and never understand that they are merely shadows of true beauty, which you neglect. You have immortal souls: why fuddle them on passing charms? See what fair creatures we are, and consider how fair must be that One to whom we minister."

" 'Indeed, my son, if you would like to lift the world's dark veil aside in order to learn wisdom from gazing on the truth, you will find in the end that all the desires you esteem the most are only childish vanity. To omit those loves which are compact of misery, as Perottino's lovers and he himself can fully illustrate, what stability or rectitude or satisfaction can the others give that we should seek or prize them so excessively as Gismondo urged that we should do? I cannot see, indeed, how all these mortal charms with which sight, hearing, and the other senses nourish the mind, allowing them to enter and re-enter it a thousand times by means of thought,—I cannot see how they avail us when they little by little overmaster us with pleasure so that we think of nothing else and, having lowered our eyes to worthless things, remain no longer true to ourselves, but change at last from men to beasts, as if we had taken the enchanted draft of Circe; nor can I understand how these charms can delight us so fully, even assuming that it is not a false delight, when they were never found nor shall be found so fully in one object that an observer might be gratified with every part and when they are rather few than tolerably free from harm.

" 'After every brief affair, moreover, they disappear in some little fever that we suffer, or at best, time bears them all away: youth, beauty, pleasure, graceful movements, tender words, songs, music, dancing, banquets, games, and all the other joys of love. They cannot fail to torture those who yearn for them, and all the more as the delights with which such lovers let themselves be haltered are the greater. If age does not rid them of these desires, what can be more wretched than to taint senility with childish wishes and animate weak, palsied limbs with callow thoughts? And if age does remove them, how foolish to love youthful things with so much ardor that one should fail to love his own maturity, or should believe that something in which the better part of life takes no delight or use is both more useful and delightful than all else? For the better part of our life, my son, is surely that in which our better part, namely the soul, is free from bondage to the appetites and rules the worser part, the body, with temperance; in which reason guides the senses, which in the heat of youth will never hear its voice but blunder turbulently here and there at will. Concerning this, I, who have been a young man too, as you are now, can give you ample proof; and when I remember the things which at that time I was accustomed to desire and praise the most, they seem more paltry to me now than one who is well recovered finds the wishes which possessed him in the height of fever, wishes of which he now makes sport, knowing how far he wandered then from knowledge and good taste.

" 'It may be said therefore that old age is the health and youth the illness of our lives, the truth of which will strike you when you reach my years, if you cannot already understand it. To return, however, to your companion who in his discourse has exalted the many joys of lovers to the heavens, let us say only that the least of them are attended with a thousand discomforts; but when, even amid his most consummate pleasures, does he not sigh for something more? or when does that conformity of wills, that community of thought about their lot, that lifelong harmony occur between two lovers? For there is no man who does not have some disagreement with himself each day, sometimes of such a sort that if one could leave himself as two can leave each other, many would do so, taking another mind and body.

" 'To come to your loves also, Lavinello: I would praise them indeed and partly enter into your view if they made you desire some more useful object than the one they set before you and if they pleased you not so much for themselves as because an understanding of them can bring us to a more perfect and less fallible condition. For virtuous love is not merely desire of beauty, as you believe, but desire of true beauty, which is not of that human and mortal kind which fades, but is immortal and divine; and yet these beauties that you praise may lift us to it, provided we regard them in the proper way. In that case what can be said in praise of them which does not fall beside the mark since men enamored of their charms leave human life behind, like gods? For those men are gods, my son, who as divinities scorn mortal things and as mortals aspire to things divine; who advise, discuss, foresee, take thought about eternity; who move and rule and moderate the body which is given them, just as the other gods dispose of things assigned to their control.

"'And yet what beauty found among us can be so pleasant and entire, what fine proportion of the parts in some human receptacle, what harmonious conformity, that it could ever fill or satisfy our hearts completely? O Lavinello, Lavinello, you are not what this external form reveals, and other men likewise are not what they may outwardly appear; the soul of each is what he is, and not the body which is there for any finger to point out. Our souls are not of such a quality that they are able to conform and satisfy themselves with any beauty found down here. If you could put all of them there are before your mind and let it choose among them and correct at will whatever seemed amiss in any part, you would not satisfy it in the end, nor would you be any happier with earthly pleasures you had gathered far and wide than you are wont to be with those you now enjoy. Souls, being immortal, can never be contented with a mortal thing.

"'But as all the stars draw light from the sun, all beauties which exist outside of the divine, eternal beauty are derived from it; and when our minds perceive these secondary beauties, they are pleased and gladly study them as likenesses and sparks of it, but they are never wholly satisfied with them because they yearn for that divine, eternal loveliness which they remember and for which they are ever secretly spurred on to search. Just as when a hungry man is overcome by sleep, he cannot satisfy his appetite by dreaming that he eats, since his hunger requires the food itself and not its likeness, so while we seek true beauty and true pleasure, which are elsewhere, we do not feed but only fool the soul by pursuing their mere shadows in these corporeal beauties and these mundane pleasures. This we must take care to avoid, in order that our good genius may not grow angry with us and abandon us to our evil one when he sees that we bear more love to the surface of one little face and to these wretched and deceitful charms than to that mighty splendor whose ray is called the sun or to its true and everlasting beauties. This life of ours is even a kind of sleep; and just as those who lie down late at night with the thought of rising early on the morrow will dream of getting up and thus while still asleep will rise and begin to draw their mantles on, so in our very dreams we strive to find, not the mere likeness of food or these vain and shadowy delights, but food itself and firm and pure contentment, and they begin to nourish us while we are still asleep, so that when we are awakened, we may give pleasure to the Queen of the Fortunate Isles.—But perhaps you have not already heard of this queen?'

" 'No, father, I don't seem to remember her, nor do I understand the pleasure of which you speak.'

" 'Then you will hear about it now,' the holy man pursued. 'Among their most esoteric memories, the ancients who were wise in sacred things held that on those islands which I have called Fortunate there was a queen of surpassing beauty, adorned with costly garments and ever young, who still remained a virgin, not wishing for a husband, but well contented to be loved and sought. And to those who loved her more she gave a greater reward; to the others one suitable to their affection. But she tested all of them as follows:

" 'When each had come before her, as she had had them summoned one by one, she touched them with a wand and sent them off; and as soon as they had left the palace, they fell asleep and remained asleep until she had them wakened. When they returned to her presence once more, each had written on his forehead an exact description of his dreams which she instantly read. And those whose dreams she saw to have dealt only with hunting, fishing, horses, forests, and wild beasts she drove from her, commanding them to spend their waking hours among the creatures of which they made companions in their sleep; for she said that if they had loved her, they would have dreamed of her at least once and that since they had never done so, she would have them live with their beasts. Of those others whose dreams had evidently been concerned with trade or governing their families and communities or similar things, yet little with the queen herself, she appointed one to be a merchant, one a citizen, one an elder in his city, weighing them down with heavy thoughts and taking no more care for them than they for her. But those who had dreamed they were with her she kept about her court to talk to her amid music, songs, and rounds of endless pleasure, one nearer and one further off according as they had spent a larger or a smaller portion of their dreams with her.

" 'But perhaps I am delaying you too much now,

Lavinello, when you must wish or need rather to return to your companions than to hear me any longer. Moreover, it might hurt you to delay your departure till the sun is higher, for it already fills the sky with heat and is still gathering its strength.'

" 'Neither wish nor need in any way compels me to return, my father,' I hastened to put in; 'and if talking is not inconvenient for you, sure I know of nothing which I have ever done more willingly than listen to your words. And don't worry about the height of the sun, for I have only to walk downhill, which would be easy at any hour.'

" 'Old men are not wont to find talking inconvenient,' he replied, 'for it is an amusement peculiar to age; nor can anything be inconvenient to me which brings you pleasure. So let us continue.

" 'To Perottino and Gismondo, then, I would say, my son, that if they did not wish to be sent among the beasts when they woke up, they should seek some better dream than theirs is now. And as for you, Lavinello, don't assume that the queen will hold you dear when you have dreamed of her so little, wasting your sleep among these unprofitable vanities rather than employing it for some really useful purpose. Know, in fine, that your love is not virtuous. Granted that it is not evil like those which are mingled with bestial desires; still it falls short of virtue because it does not draw you toward an immortal object but holds you midway between the extremes of desire where it is not safe to remain, for on a slope it is easier to slide into the depths than to clamber to the summit. And is not one who trusts to the pleasures of some sense, although he does not intend to fall into evil ways, likely, at least at times, to be ensnared? for sense is full of deceits, making the same things appear to be sometimes good and sometimes evil, sometimes fair and sometimes foul, sometimes pleasing and sometimes spiteful. Furthermore, how can any desire be virtuous which rests on sensuous pleasures as it were on water, pleasures degrading those who have them, tormenting those who lack them, and all as fugitive as the brief moment? Nor can the fine, distinguished phrases with which such lovers speak of it change the thing itself; for even if thought perpetuate these delights, how much better it would be not to have our heavenly, immortal minds than, having them, to clog and, as it were, to bury them in earthly thoughts! They were not given us that we should nourish them on mortal poison, but rather on restorative ambrosia, whose flavor never torments or degrades, being always dear and precious. And this can happen only if we turn our souls back to that God who gave them to us.

" 'You will do so, my son, if you will listen to me and consider that He has spread Himself throughout this sacred temple which we call the earth, and in His marvelous wisdom made it circular, revolving on itself, and of itself both needy and replete. He girt it in with many spheres of purest substance which ever turn around it, the greatest moving contrariwise to all the rest; on one of them He set the countless stars which shine on every side, and to each of the other spheres assigned a star to hold, commanding all of them to draw their light from that great splendor which guides them on their courses, divides the night from day, produces time, and begets and governs all things born. He made these luminaries perform their cycles on fixed paths, completing them and, when completed, beginning them once more, each in a less or greater period. And under all of these He placed the purer element of fire and filled all that remained, from there to us, with air. And in the middle, or lowest part, He fixed the earth, as if it were the ridge of the temple, and surrounded it with the waters, which are a lighter element than earth, though heavier than air, which in its turn is heavier than fire.

" 'Here you will be delighted to determine how their four kinds of qualities are mingled through these four parts and how they simultaneously agree and disagree; delighted to study the phases of the changing moon, the labors of the sun, the varied courses of the wandering stars and of those which do not wander, and by considering the causes and the functions of them all to lead your mind around the heavens. Conversing with nature as it were, you will learn how brief and paltry are the things we love on earth, when the greatest length of this human life can hardly fill two days of one celestial year and the least star of that infinite multitude is greater than this solid sphere which we so proudly call the earth and of which, in turn, the place that we inhabit is only a microscopic particle. Here, moreover, everything is weak and sickly, what with winds, rain, ice, snow, cold, heat, fevers, colics, vomits, and other such diseases which have assailed us ever since the opening of Pandora's splendid box exposed us to these harms; while there all things are strong and reach a state so perfect that neither death nor age nor any lack can overcome them.

" 'But your delight and wonder will be even greater, Lavinello, if you can pass from these heavens which you see to those which are unseen and contemplate the things which are actually there, ascending from one to another until you raise your desires to that beauty which surpasses them and every other beauty. For those who are used to gazing with the eyes of the soul no less than of the body have no doubt that beyond this sensible, material world of which I have spoken, as everyone speaks more often of what he sees, there lies another world which is neither material nor evident to sense, but completely separate from this and pure; a world which turns around this one and is both sought and found by it, wholly divided from it and wholly abiding in each part of it; a world divine, intelligent, and full of light, itself as much beyond itself in size and virtue as it draws nearer to its Final Cause.

" 'That world contains all that we have in this, but things as much more excellent than these as the heavenly are better than the earthly here. For just as this world has its earth, so that has its green earth too which puts forth plants and feeds its animals and has its sea to mingle with, its ambient air, its fire, its moon, its sun, its stars, its other spheres. But there the grass is never brown, the plants are never withered, the creatures never die, the seas are never rough, the air is never dark, the fire never parches, nor must its heavens and their bodies turn continually. That world has no need of any change, for neither summer nor winter, nor yesterday nor tomorrow, nor near nor far, nor large nor small confines it; but it rests contented with its state, having achieved the highest self-sufficiency and happiness, and being big with it, gives birth to this very world you see before you. And if we think that there can be no other than the one we see, we are like a man who having spent his days from birth deep in the abysm of the sea, would for that reason be unable to imagine by himself that there were other things above the water, nor would believe that elsewhere he might find branches fairer than seaweed, or meadows more delightful than the sands, or animals more gay than fish, or habitations of another kind than stony caverns, or other elements than earth and water.

" 'But were he to rise into our region and see the vivid greenery of fields and woods and hills; the variety of creatures, some born to feed us and some to aid us; the cities, temples, houses standing here; the many arts and ways of life; the purity of the air; the brilliance of the sun which by scattering its light through heaven, makes the day and kindles the stars with which the darkness of the night is splendid; and all the other so various and endless beauties of the world,—he would understand how mistaken he had been and would not wish his old life back at any price. So we wretches who are assigned to live upon this filthy ball of earth, seeing the air and the birds who cleave it, feel the same wonder as that with which he views the ocean and its fish; and in the same way we consider all the various beauties of those heavens which we see only in part. Beside all these, however, we have many more things to admire than our ocean man would find on earth, things marvelous and dear whose what or how our poor intelligence can never grasp. Yet were some god to carry us up there and show them to us,

Lavinello, only those would seem real to us, and the life led there the true one, and all that is here, but a shadow or picture of their existence; and gazing down from that serene height on other men among these shadows here below, we would call ourselves wretched and pity them, nor ever willingly return to such a life.

" 'But what can I say to you, Lavinello? You are young, and in youth, apparently, such thoughts do not take root; or if they do, they for the most part grow poorly, as if they had been planted in the shade. Nevertheless, if they should enter your youthful mind when you are charmed down here by the dim light of two eyes already full of death, what must you make of those eternal splendors which are so true, so pure, so mild? And if the sound of some tongue delights you which caused you to weep only a little earlier and which will be silent soon forever, how precious must you find the discourse and the harmony made by the heavenly choruses in unison? And when you take such satisfaction from thinking of some silly woman's doings, one like so many here, what satisfaction do you think your soul would take if it were to purify itself of these delusions and in its innocence to reach those shining forms, to gaze with growing concentration on the great works of that Lord who rules above, and to bring its chaste affections and desires as an offering to Him?

" 'This pleasure is too great, my son, for anyone to understand who has not proved it, and none can prove it who cares a straw for other pleasures. For the sun cannot be endured by such mole's eyes as those with which our souls, blindfolded by their longings, see; nay, even the most clear-sighted does not reach that far. But some stranger, passing before the palace of a king, even though he cannot see or otherwise know that it belongs to a king, surmises that some great man must live there, since he sees it full of servants, and thinks him greater as those servants are more dignified and dressed more richly; in the same way, although we cannot see that mighty Lord at all, we can yet say that He must be a mighty lord since all the elements and all the heavens minister to Him and serve His majesty. Therefore, your friends will do wisely if they will henceforth court this Prince as they have wooed their ladies hitherto, and if remembering that they are in a temple, they will now dispose themselves to pray since they have had enough of vanities, and casting aside false, earthly, mortal love, will clothe themselves in that which is true, celestial, and immortal. And this it would be well for you to do likewise.

" 'For every good accompanies this heavenly desire, and every ill is far from it. There none encounter rivalries, suspicions, or jealousies since, however many love Him, many more may love Him also and enjoy their love as thoroughly as one alone would do; that infinite Godhead can satisfy us all and yet remain eternally the same. There none need fear treachery or harm or broken faith. Nothing unsuitable is sought, or granted, or desired. The body receives what is sufficient, as Cerberus is thrown a biscuit lest he bark; and the soul enjoys what it requires most. Nor is anyone forbidden to seek what he loves or denied the power to attain that delight to which his love impels him. Nor do men go by land and sea, or climb on walls or roofs, to find what they desire. Nor is there need of arms or messenger or escort; for God is all that each can see or wish. Neither anger nor scorn nor repentance nor change nor joy deceptive nor vain hope nor grief nor fear is found there. There neither chance nor fortune can prevail. There all is full of certainty, content, and happiness.

" 'And those things which other men love so much down here and to secure which we so often see the whole world thrown into confusion, the very streams run red with human blood, and even the ocean on occasion, as this wretched age of ours has often known and still knows, for that matter,—empires and crowns and lordships, I mean—: these are no more sought by one of our celestial lovers than he who can have water from a pure wellspring, when he is thirsty will seek that of some turbid, marshy rivulet. If, on the other hand, poverty, exile, or oppression overtakes him, as one who dwells here sees befalling every day, he receives it with a smile, remembering that it makes little difference which cloth covers or land contains or wall encloses this body, and that the little love he bears such things does not deprive the mind of its wealth, its country, or its freedom. In brief, he neither welcomes happy circumstances with too much delight nor equally refuses to live out the bitter ones, but temperately endures them both as long as the Lord who gave them wills that he should linger here. And while other lovers fear death throughout their lives as something which will bring all their revels to an end, and make that journey, when they reach it, with melancholy and unwillingness, he goes there joyfully when he is called, believing he has changed a wretched inn for his own house that overflows with gladness and festivity. And what if not an inn can this life be called, which is rather a kind of death through which we journey, with all its grievances assailing us from every side so often, with all its constant partings from what we love the most, with all its deaths from day to day of those who are most dear to us, with all its other mishaps that every hour give us reason to weep, and these more often the more we think we ought to be enjoying peace and pleasure?

" 'You can tell how far this is true of your own case. To me indeed it seems a thousand years before I can unloose the wrapping of my flesh, and flying from this prison or deceitful inn, return to the place from which I came, and when the eyesight lost upon this journey is recovered, can see that indescribable beauty which I, thanks to its own beneficence, have loved so long already. And though I am an old man now, as you perceive, it holds me no less dear than it has always done nor will deny me because I come before it in such a humble garb. Not that I shall go there in this form, any more than you will go in yours; for no one takes anything beside his loves from here. And if they are attached to these beauties here below, they torment us since they cannot rise upward but are fixed in the earth which bore them, just as we are now tormented by desires which cannot in the least be satisfied. If our loves are, on the other hand, celestial, they bring a marvelous contentment since we can reach them and enjoy them fully. Nay, furthermore, our future state is everlasting, Lavinello, and so we must believe that virtuous love is to be eternally enjoyed and that the other which is evil damns us to eternal grief.'

"When the holy man had said so much, he allowed me to depart, for it was time that I should do so." And with these words Lavinello brought his discourse to a close.

FINIS

Index

WHEN a name listed in this index does not actually appear in the English or Italian text, identifying or cue words are given in parentheses. For some of the identifications I am indebted to Carlo Dionisotti-Casalone's edition of *Gli Asolani e le Rime* (Turin, 1932).

DATE DUE

GAYLORD | | | PRINTED IN U.S.A.